GRASS-ROOTS OF AGRICULTURAL AND COMMUNITY DEVELOPMENT PROGRAMME IN INDIA

GRASS-ROOTS OF AGRICULTURAL AND COMMUNITY DEVELOPMENT PROGRAMME IN INDIA

by
Ram Krishan

ALLIED PUBLISHERS PRIVATE LIMITED
BOMBAY—NEW DELHI—CALCUTTA—MADRAS
LONDON—NEW YORK

First Published 1966

ALLIED PUBLISHERS PRIVATE LIMITED
15, Graham Road, Ballard Estate, Bombay-1.
13/14, Asaf Ali Road, New Delhi-1.
17, Chittaranjan Avenue, Calcutta-13.
38-C, Mount Road, Madras-6.

PRINTED IN INDIA

by M. K. Kulkarni, B.Sc., at Displaycraft, 109-A, Industrial Area,
Sion, Bombay 22, and Published by R. N. Sachdev for Allied Publishers
Private Limited, 15, Graham Road, Ballard Estate, Bombay-1.

PREFACE

THE PROGRAMME of community development was started in the country on October 2, 1952, the birthday of Mahatma Gandhi. The programme has been one of the major undertakings of the Union Government to initiate a process of transformation in the social and economic life of the rural people. It was new but its concept grew out a series of experiments in rural development conducted in Madras (Firka Development Scheme), Uttar Pradesh (Etawah Pilot Project), Bombay (Sarvodaya Scheme), West Bengal (at Shantiniketan), Punjab (at Nilokheri) and in the country as 'Grow-More-Food Campaign' launched by the Government of India in the late thirties. The unique feature of the new programme has been a co-ordinated, integrated and comprehensive approach to all problems of the rural people.

The programme was launched with a modest beginning. Public enthusiasm in response to it was heartening. It was, therefore, allowed to expand afterwards on a large scale in response to the pressing needs of the country and Sri S. K. Dey brought ardent zeal to the task of giving it a tangible shape.

The original plan was to cover the entire country with blocks by the end of the Second Five-Year Plan, but in view of the repeated warnings of the Programme Evaluation Organisation —an independent organisation working under the Planning Commission — and the recommendation of the Committee on Planned Projects, the National Development Council decided to revise the programme and deferred the coverage of the country with blocks* from March 1961 to October 1963.

The contents and methods of the programme have also undergone considerable changes since the first 53 community projects were started in 1952. In October 1953, a national ex-

---

*A block in this country is a unit of development comprising an area having a population of about 60 to 70 thousand people.

tension service (N.E.S.) was established. In addition, 53
community development blocks were also started. The budget
allotment and pattern of staff have also undergone considerable
changes since then. On the recommendation of the Committee
on Planned Projects, the distinction between the national extension service and community development stages was abolished.
Instead, only two stages of block development were envisaged.
These were termed stage I and stage II. Stage I was for a
period of five years with a budget provision of Rs. 1.2 million.
Stage II was for a further period of five years, but with a budget
provision of Rs. 0.5 million. In view of the emphasis on agricultural production, each stage-I-block was to have a pre-extension
period of one to two years to concentrate more or less on
agricultural development.

Further modifications will continue to be made in the programme as new problems arise and the content of the programme
is changed to correct mistakes and deficiencies that are noticed
from time to time.

Experience shows that the progress of this programme is
greatly affected by four important factors besides several others.
They are:

  (I)   The people.
  (II) The programmes.
  (III) The attitude and outlook of the official machinery (im-
        mediate and higher bosses) towards extension program-
        mes and problems of the people and subordinates.
  (IV) The extension worker.

These four factors have, therefore, been made the subject
matter of this book and are discussed under separate chapters
in relation to this programme.

The start of the programme was a great trial in which the
country pinned and still pins great hopes. The programme as
such was regarded as harbinger of socio-economic emancipation and of a socialistic pattern of society in the country. This

programme has ever since its inception been a dynamic process. Several shortcomings and mistakes crept into the programme in the course of its execution. Many of these mistakes were due to inadequate experience and rapid expansion. That was to some extent inevitable in a vast and dynamic programme like this. Mistakes may be unavoidable, but if a constant watch is kept and mistakes are remedied, programmes develop faster and in a better way than otherwise.

No account of community development programme can be complete unless it succeeds in showing how best defects and shortcomings can be remedied. An earnest effort has been made in this book to deal with them also and to suggest simple measures to remove them.

Those persons, communities, organisations and governments who constantly review their programmes, and do little bit of heart searching to find out their own mistakes, rectify them, make a constant endeavour not to repeat them and create a healthier climate for work, rise, succeed and make a mark for the future to remember. Those who amuse themselves over small successes, carry out extensive propaganda even of minor things for self-publicity and try to hide their mistakes for fear of loss of prestige and reputation, do succeed temporarily but ultimately fail and lose the race. When they fail, they blame the programme to be unworkable and impractical and substitute it with a new one or change it drastically. This is a grave mistake. Programmes once started after considerable thinking and study should be continued till success is achieved with them and they should be abandoned only after full trial and maximum effort counsel such a course. At every stage of progress made, there should be a full review of the programme; shortcomings should be taken note of and rectified, and the lessons carefully remembered.

Where mistakes have been made and detected, idle critics are apt to indulge in wholesale condemnation of the programme itself and the performance of the workers. This kind of criticism should not be allowed to disturb the equanimity of anyone.

Honest and sincere workers will find no offence in some of
the frank exposures of situations which called for exposure in
this book. They are, in fact, untypical and serve only as warnings. Undoubtedly there are exceptions always, but what has
been observed may have general application. Those fortunate
few who have successfully avoided these mistakes owe a duty to
their fellow workers. They should clearly point the way to
avoid those mistakes so that even the average worker may be able
to make a success of his opportunities by dint of determination
and confidence.

Let us hope that the book will succeed in stimulating some
fresh thinking, and help in reviewing the common mistakes (which
because they are so common we stop noticing and thinking about),
that it will quicken the tempo of the programme and put new
heart into those who are engaged in making the community
development programme a success.

The author has been associated with the programme of community development right from its inception in October 1952.
Most of the material contained in this book was collected by
him in the capacity of an active participant in this programme
in Uttar Pradesh.

It will repay the labours of the author in the writing of this
book if it succeeds in bringing home to everyone connected with
the community development programme in India, from the highest
planners to the humble worker in the field, the factors in the
situation which have, with few exceptions, brought the
'Blossoms into dust'.

The author is thankful to his various colleagues for helping
to improve the subject-matter of this book and the various
sources for material utilised in this book. The author is especially
grateful to Sri Ram Sahay, Commissioner & Secretary, Agriculture, Government of U.P., for his inspiring and loving guidance in improving the contents of this book. Special thanks are
also due to Sri J. D. Shukla, Commissioner, Allahabad Division,
Dr. R. K. Tandon, Additional Director of Agriculture and Sri

M. S. Haq, Dy. Development Commissioner (Central Zone), Lucknow, Uttar Pradesh, for going through the manuscript with great patience and thoroughness and suggesting various improvements. Sri Haq specially has been my senior colleague working in the community development programme right from its inception. His suggestions were, therefore, of immense help to me.

Thanks are also due to Sri Ishwar Sahai Srivastava and Sri Habibullah for typing the manuscript.

RAM KRISHAN

CONTENTS

CHAPTER I

THE PEOPLE

1. *Organisational set-up of the people*

THE PEOPLE in rural India live in small settlements called ham-
lets, villages and in some cases towns. They consist of populations
ranging from a few hundred to a few thousand. The people living
in these settlements are seldom a homogeneous mass; they are
in fact divided into several socio-economic groups on the basis
of kinship, religion, caste, sex, profession, neighbourhood affini-
ties, *etc*. The primary unit of these groups is the family. When
there is a change in membership from one group to another,
it is generally the whole family and seldom the individual which
shifts allegiance from one group to the other. Each of these groups
can be distinguished by characteristic traditions, customs, habits,
values and their social and economic pattern of life. By functioning as separate socio-economic units, these groups have developed a remarkable stability over the years. Making changes in
the socio-economic dispositions of the group is generally not a
matter for individuals to decide, but for the group as a whole,
even though a particular individual or a few belonging to the
group may desire change.

Besides socio-economic groups, there are also power and
prestige groups formed just for trials of strength and vindication
of prestige. These groups also play a very important part in
the life of the whole community. Such groups or factions are
formed by members belonging to different socio-economic groups.
Often socio-economic groups may be pitted against one another
just on prestige issue.

1

2. *Effect of socio-economic groups in villages on extension of programmes*

The organisational set up of the different socio-economic groups or factions in the villages is a complicated affair. It determines to a great extent the attitude of the people towards adoption of programmes. There are several castes in India which do not carry out a few of the important operations concerning their profession. For those who are agriculturists, ploughing is one such operation. Sheikhs among Muslims and Brahmins and Thakurs among Hindus, especially in the eastern and central districts of Uttar Pradesh and parts of Bihar, do not touch the plough with their hands. They get all their holdings ploughed up through hired labour. On account of their dependence on hired labour, they are seldom able to carry out their agricultural operations in time. They also do not get the maximum from their holdings.

There are several castes or professional groups which have specialized in certain professions over a period of time. For example *Kurmis* in Uttar Pradesh are very good vegetable growers. The people belonging to this caste are mostly well-to-do persons and are open to new ideas about their profession.

Old traditions in the country have resulted in the desire to become and remain rich without doing any hard work. This state of mind has been fostered by the fact that persons, who do manual labour in our country, are looked down upon in society and do not earn as much respect as those who are rich and do not work with their own hands. This tendency leads people to aspire for easy short-cuts to wealth and the prestige of leadership by concentrating their energies mainly on advising and preaching to others coming under their influence and professing to help them by making common cause with them at their cost. These aspirations, coupled with the lust for money and power, result, in the absence of any significant productive contribution to society, in the employment of unfair means to achieve desired ends. These in turn lead in many cases to corruption, lawlessness, feuds on account of the creation of power and prestige groups, even sometimes to crime, and considerable wastage of time and resources which otherwise would have gone into productive work. Because of the sense of insecurity springing from rivalries, people tend to move in groups and plan and work against the rival groups at the cost of their valuable time, existing resources and additional new resources generated from their new productive pursuits if any.

Besides the direct reaction of socio-economic groups on the expansion of programmes in the villages, their inherent characteristics depending upon traditions, customs, beliefs and outlook also determine their attitude towards the sponsored programmes. The study of these factors in regard to their effects upon programmes is very necessary before making any beginning with the community. Utter ignorance or even lack of understanding may make the groups reject an idea outright although it may be technically and also otherwise sound and feasible.

The programme of composting animal and vegetable refuse in India is a typical example of how the factors mentioned above operate. It is proposed to analyse them in some detail below:

Animal and vegetable refuse in India is generally stored in heaps located near houses or on the outskirts of the village. Manure prepared by storing it in heaps and leaving it exposed to the weather, contains about 0.3 to 0.4 per cent nitrogen as compared to 0.5 to 0.7 per cent nitrogen by the improved method of storing it in pits. Of the cow-dung produced in India, about 60 per cent is converted into dung cakes which are used as fuel or for plastering *kutcha* houses and floors with. If all the dung was stored in pits and utilized for composting on improved lines, the country could have about 5 million tons of additional nitrogen through proper utilization of its existing resources only.

Stress on the preparation of compost from the available animal and vegetable refuse has been laid by different government departments in the country for more than 40 years now. The success of this programme has, however, not been very encouraging. The matter still continues to be stressed in every agricultural campaign; so much so that field workers have now come to take it as a routine programme. A separate scheme for the development of local manurial resources has also been recently launched in all the States of the country with this item of compost-making from animal and vegetable refuse occupying a prominent place in it.

The following reasons can be advanced for poor response in the villages to this programme:

(a) *Economic*:

    (*i*) Lack of availability of alternative fuel. As already stated, approximately 60 per cent of the cow-dung in our villages is converted into dung cakes for fuel and for plastering houses and floors with. Burning of cow-dung cakes is an economic necessity and cannot be avoided because the people do not have any alternative fuel. Where there is an alternative source of fuel, cow-dung is seldom used as fuel, for example, in the hill districts of Uttar Pradesh, Punjab, Bihar and Assam.

    (*ii*) Non-availability of land for making compost pits within walking distance of the houses.

    (*iii*) Use of its smoke for driving out mosquitoes, flies and other insects from houses and cattle barns.

    (*iv*) Use of ignited cow-dung cake as a substitute for matches because once it is ignited it continues to burn till the end.

(b) *Habit*:

    (*i*) Habit of *Hookah* smoking and preferring dung cake fire for it.

    (*ii*) Habit of storing refuse as near the houses as possible for convenience.

(c) *Custom*:

    (*i*) Prevalent custom of *Ghee* (clarified butter) making for which slow and steady fire produced by dung cake is preferred.

    (*ii*) Prevalent custom of plastering walls of houses, floors with cow-dung, *etc.*

(d) *Tradition*:

    (*i*) The work of cleaning houses and cattle-yards and depositing the refuse in the villages is traditionally the work of womenfolk. They do not like to carry loads of refuse from the cattle-yard all the way to the compost pits or heaps located generally away from their houses. They, therefore, dump this refuse near about their houses which leads to insanitary conditions and wastage of manurial ingredients through exposure to sun, rain and air. Though the menfolk realise the importance of manure, they do not like to handle it because it is customary for the womenfolk only to handle it.

(e) *Value*:

The work of preparing compost is considered to be inferior to other jobs and, therefore, little attention is paid to it in spite of the fact that they appreciate its importance.

It would appear from the above facts that various socio-economic factors are involved as the result of which the programme of compost making is not gaining momentum. Unless, therefore, the programme is tackled thoroughly, taking into consideration all the factors mentioned above, it is not likely to succeed. Because the programme has not so far been handled in this manner, the progress has not been very appreciable in spite of the fact that constant pressure of persuasion and advice has been exerted on the people during the last 40 years or so as to adopt it.

The whole stress of the extension machinery at the present time is mainly on the digging of pits and the storing of refuse in them. The pits once dug give way after a year or two due to the weathering effect of the sun, rain and air, and thus the people automatically revert to the old habit of storing refuse in heaps. The progress achieved in any one year comes to naught after a year or two and thus the cycle goes on every year.

The practice of merely getting compost pits dug and reporting their number in progress reports has now become a mechanical affair for the last several years. In spite of the very limited success achieved so far, the programme continues to be stressed in the same manner as in the past and has not been tackled properly to remove the causes which stand in its way.

The above example clearly shows how social customs, traditions, habits and values and economic factors play a great part in the people's acceptance of programmes. It is for this reason that the extension worker has to take these factors into consideration, study them in detail before a particular programme is launched and take steps to counteract them.

In view of what has been said above, the programme of composting in rural areas has to be tackled from different angles before some success can be expected. A few important points in this connection are given below:

(a) Providing additional fuel resources by:

    (i) Planting fuel trees and popularizing plants which provide both fuel and some kind of economic produce, for example cotton, arhar, dhaincha, indigo, etc.

    (ii) Popularizing use of kerosene oil *Chulhas*, combustible gases wherever available and coal.

    (iii) Popularizing cow-dung gas plants.

    (iv) Enjoining on each *Gaon Panchayat* to have a minimum of fuel reserve in its area. Land for fuel plantation should be separately earmarked during the course of consolidation of holdings.

(b) Arranging land for digging of compost pits.

(c) Popularizing construction of *pucca* compost pits.

(d) Educating people—men and women—in the importance of compost making.

(e) Popularizing the use of wheel barrows for carting refuse so that womenfolk may not carry it on their heads.

(f) Changing habits:

    (i) Popularizing new methods of *ghee* manufacture.

    (ii) Trying to substitute *Hookah* with other methods of smoking.

(g) Planting *Ipomea carnia* and other useful plants around pits to produce additional organic matter for composting.

(h) Encouraging collection of dry and fallen leaves and putting them in compost pits.

3. *Effect of power and prestige groups and leadership in villages on extension of programmes*

Besides the socio-economic factors, the acceptance of programme is also very much dependent upon leadership including power and prestige groups and associations working in the villages. It is necessary to make a detailed study of their structure, pulls and stresses that they exercise and take advantage of this knowledge in pushing up the programmes in the light of the existing social, religious and cultural peculiarities and angularities.

The leaders provide an excellent channel through which the people can be approached by the extension workers for acceptance of programmes. Approaching leaders for acceptance of programmes and getting a success through them is easier than approaching each family direct. The extension worker has neither the time nor the resources to do so. Hence, the need of approaching the people through their leaders, even though a direct approach may be better under certain circumstances. Not all leaders are helpful in pushing up programmes. They, therefore, have to be very carefully selected.

(*a*) *Kinds of leaders*:

There are generally four types of leaders available in villages:
- (*i*) Elected leaders,
- (*ii*) Leaders by virtue of their technical knowledge and skills,
- (*iii*) Leaders by virtue of their personal qualities, and
- (*iv*) Self-appointed leaders.

(*i*) *Elected leaders*:

The elected leaders are those leaders who are put in a position of leadership to serve as a member or an office-holder of a statutory or non-statutory organization or committee. These leaders are either chosen by election on the basis of votes or are selected by government or a non-official organization to represent them. Some of the important leaders and organizations that matter in agricultural and community development in India are:

Leaders	Organizations
1. President	1. Village Panchayat
2. Vice-President	2. -do-
3. *Sarpanch*	3. *Nyaya Panchayat*
4. *Panchas*	4. -do-
5. *Sarpanch* and other office-holder	5. Co-operative Society
6. *Pradhan* and delegates	6. Cane Union
7. *Pramukh* and *Up-Pramukh*	7. *Kshetra Samiti*
8. Convener	8. *Bharat Sevak Samaj*
9. *Pradhan* or some other office-holder	9. Youth club
10. Member	10. Legislative Assembly
11. Member	11. Legislative Council
12. Member	12. Parliament
13. *Pradhan* or *Adhyaksh*	13. *Zila Parishad*

As the community in villages consists of groups and sub-groups within the groups, the elected leaders in most of the cases are mere leaders of a group or a sub-group and cannot in most cases be called general leaders respected by the entire community. If the election of these leaders is unanimous, and by secret ballot, there are generally no factional rivalries, but if it is not unanimous, the result often is serious group rivalries and factions. If the leader is elected after defeating more than one candidate, he usually does not command the respect of the majority of the community, but only of a section. If such a leader is entrusted with the responsibility of execution of a pro-gramme, he generally faces resistance from other sections and groups which he does not represent.

The resistance may not be on the ground that the programme is uneconomical or socially and culturally unsuitable, but may simply be a result of traditional rivalries between groups and factions as the result of which opposite groups do not co-operate. If the extension worker is wise and understands the situation, he tries to get hold of the leaders of opposing groups and factions individually and then brings them together in a meeting for a common cause and for the good of the entire community or the village. The leaders of opposing groups and factions in the village or elsewhere may either be made to come together and iron out their differences to provide for the commonly felt needs, or, if they do not come and agree to work together, they may work separately for the common objective and compete with each other in the execution of the programme through their own groups and factions. If somehow a spirit of competition is created in the leaders, the work goes on smoothly, provided the enthusiasm of each faction is channelised by the extension worker on healthy lines. If the spirit of healthy competition between the different groups or factions is not developed, or the opposing groups do not agree to work together, some workers try to work through one or two groups only. The success of projects in such cases—patronising one or two factional groups only—is limited to the achievement of the co-operating group only. Such a success is only partial and is not very lasting, as it rests not on the desire for betterment among the people, but on the not very laudable motive of not allowing the rival group to gain any advantage.

The elected leader in the village where there is keen rivalry for leadership is often not the real leader of the village although he may be the leader of the majority. If it is only a bare majority, he is not able to function properly because he is under the obligation of his supporters and he tries to support them even if he has to go out of his way to do so. Factional rivalries in such a situation increase and most of the time of the leaders is spent in manoeuvring position rather than in constructive work.

These leaders sometimes prove to be a source of headache to the extension workers because of their influence with some important political leaders. They sometimes also threaten the extension worker with dire consequences if he does not bow to their wishes. The worker tends to be demoralised as a result, for if he obeys them he is violating the promptings of his own conscience; if he does not, he must pay the price of his independence.

Some such leaders also keep contact with persons or organization held in popular esteem. They also pose as agents of various administrative branches. People come to them for redress if they are in difficulties, and those who are helped by them naturally feel indebted to them.

(ii) Leaders by virtue of technical knowledge and skill:

These are people who have achieved leadership by virtue of some special distinction in some field such as sports, art, science, *etc.* For example, one may be a good doctor, a *Vaid* or a *Hakim,* a singer, a dramatist, a good farmer, a good teacher or a priest, *etc.* People come and sit with them. Such leaders, by virtue of the fact that people are attracted by their special distinction, have considerable direct influence on them.

(iii) Leaders by virtue of their private and independent position:

These are those leaders who do not hold any official position but are nevertheless consulted on all important decisions taken by a group or a faction leader. These leaders are in the majority of the cases more important leaders than the elected leaders. They are generally the decision makers of a group or a faction in the villages. These leaders must be taken into confidence by the extension workers besides others, for extending their programmes.

Some social workers and caste *Panchayat* leaders belong to this group and occupy an important place in the community. Among them may be money-lenders, priests, and faction leaders, ex-*Zamindars,* ex-service men, *etc.*

(iv) Self-appointed or opportunist leaders:

The self-appointed leaders are those who think themselves, and pose, as leaders and volunteer their services for any programme whatsoever. Such leaders do not have any following and are generally persons who have plenty of spare time. They angle for the friendship and patronage of the extension worker or his higher officer, in order to gain influence over fellow villagers. Some of them consort with undesirable elements and may easily fall into the temptation of selling their services at some settled price for helping people from the clutches of bad persons. They owe their position to their nuisance value.

(*b*) *Personal characteristics of the leaders* :

The personal qualities of the leaders have a great bearing on the success of welfare or economic programmes in the villages. Their age, parentage, social status, caste, their public record of sacrifice, personal qualities, educational qualifications, and wealth possessed by them count a lot towards the influence or authority they are able to exercise in the village by virtue of their being an elected or non-elected leader.

The Programme Evaluation Organisation of the Planning Commission, Government of India, in a survey carried out in 1958, studied the personal characteristics of the 547 *panchayat*[1] members and 47 *panchayat* presidents in 60 *Panchayats* of 15 Extension Blocks spread all over the country. The salient points brought out by this study were :

(*i*) *Panchayat members* :

(1) The majority (59.8%) of the *Panchayat* members were above 40 years old. About 39% were in the age groups between 25 and 40 years, and only 1% below 25 years of age. This meant that the leadership and the responsibility for taking decisions in the villages were concentrated mainly in the hands of the older people. This is perhaps due to the fact that such people have more experience and maturity of wisdom and have relatively more spare time than the younger people who look after the day-to-day work of the house and cultivation.

(2) Of the 547 members, 42.2% were illiterate, 36.4% had read up to primary standard, 17.0% up to middle standard, 2.9% upto matric and 1.5% above matric. Literacy among the *Panchayat* members on the whole was found to be higher than among the adult males of the villages. Of the literate persons, about 63% had read upto primary standard only.

(3) Of the 547 members, 69.8% came from higher castes and 30.2% from the lower castes. Out of the high-caste members, the majority were the principal land-owners of the villages.

(4) Of the 547 members, 88.1% were land-holders and only 11.9% non-land holders.

[1] A study of Panchayats—Programme Evaluation Organisation, Planning Commission (Publication number 28, May, 1958).

(ii) Panchayat presidents:

(1) Of the 47 presidents under study, 46.8% were between the ages of 25 to 40 years and the remaining 53.2%, 40 years or above 40 years of age.

(2) Of the 47 presidents, 17.0% were illiterate, 44.7% read upto primary standard, 27.7% upto middle, 8.5% upto matric and 2.1% above matric standard.

(3) Of the 47 presidents, 95.7% were land-holders and 4.3% non-land holders.

(4) Of the 47 presidents 97.9% belonged to high-caste group and 2.1% to low-caste group.

(5) Of the 47 presidents, 89.4% were reported to be rich from the village standard and 10.6% not so rich or with ordinary means.

It would appear from the above study of the Programme Evaluation Organisation of the Planning Commission that:

(1) Decisions in the villages are taken mostly by the older people.

(2) Most of the leaders are illiterate or have read only up to primary or middle standard.

(3) Most of these leaders are big land-holders (81.1% in the case of *Panchayat* members and 89.4% in the case of *Panchayat* presidents).

(4) Most of the leaders belong to high castes.

The study also revealed that although the Presidents could play an important role in the execution of the development programmes in the villages, they are handicapped in this role because many of them are not qualified to carry on the functions entailed by the post. In many cases they were not aware of the *Panchayat* laws. This resulted in their dependence upon the *Panchayat* Secretary to a great extent. The development programmes, therefore, instead of being the affair of the President, became also the responsibility of the *Panchayat* Secretary who in a way plays a more important role than the President. As the majority of the Presidents are uneducated or only partly educated, they depend upon the *Panchayat* Secretaries for interpreting the rules and Government orders. This dependence makes the *Panchayat* Secretary, rather than the President, the real leader. It is noticed that many a time programmes are undertaken by the Presidents in the villages because the *Panchaya*t Secretary has asked them to take them up.

Majumdar[2] (1962) studied in the district of Lucknow (U.P.) the qualities of a few recognised village leaders and the factors that contributed to their prestige. The description of these qualities and factors as given by the author are summarised below:

(1) D.5—He is a Brahmin by caste, and is a *Panch* of the *Adalat Panchayat.* He was once very rich, but he squandered his money and is now in financial straits. He spent large amounts in leading a fast life. He also lent out large sums, and did not care to recover them. He is of somewhat reserved nature and he does not interfere in any other people's affairs unless he is called upon to mediate. He is the oldest Brahmin in the village and is held in high esteem by virtue of his office as the village priest.

(2) M. Singh (a Thakur). He owns 30 *Bighas* (about 19 acres), of agricultural land, two cows and two bullocks and a big, though *kutcha* house with two spacious courtyards and some land in front of it. He lends out large sums of money to the people in the village. His yearly income from this source is about Rs. 200. He does not press a man too much for payment either of the loan or the interest, even when he is hard pressed for money. People respect him for his influence with the police, and for his wealth, but, most of all, for his willingness to help anyone in trouble.

(3) D. Singh (*Sarpanch*). He owns jointly with his three brothers 40 *Bighas* of agricultural land and three houses. He makes many contacts and friendships which at some later date would be useful to him. He is known to accept bribes, and some people criticise him bitterly for this. In spite of this drawback, he has certain inherent qualities. It does not matter to him whether a debt is repaid or not, because he himself spends a lot of money in drinking and merry-making and on leading a fast life. He combines wealth with generosity.

[2] Majumdar, D. N. (1962), *Caste and Communication in an Indian Village* (Asia Publishing House, Bombay).

He is always willing to help others and would use even illegal means to alleviate the sufferings of those who seek his aid. Some local officials are his friends, for he greases their palms well. Thus local bad characters and criminals often escape the stern hands of the law through his help. He entertains these undesirable people at his house, but never takes part in their activities, though he claims a share in their booty for help-ing them to escape the arms of the law. He is an adept card-player, and sometimes wins as much as Rs. 400-500 a day by this means. He started gambling when he was 12 years old, and says that he has always been lucky at it. He has never been arrested for gambling and he has no fear on that score. A happy-go-lucky man, he talks very little, but whenever he talks, he speaks so convincingly and clearly that he is listened to with much respect. Generally he keeps aloof from contro-versial matters, but as a village leader he cannot always remain completely aloof. In deciding cases and settling quarrels, he is impartial and disinterested. The villagers supported him un-animously in the elections, and since he became the *Sarpanch*, his prestige has greatly increased. Another quality in him is that when he helps someone he does it in such a way that the recipient of his help feels obliged to him and respects him.

(4) **B**. Singh and **M**. Singh. They are brothers, not very rich but quite influential in the village. In general, they are honest, straightforward and helpful but if rubbed the wrong way, they can be dangerous. They are alleged to have killed a Baniya[3] a few years back. They had taken a loan from him and the Baniya, thinking them to be ignorant, tried to cheat them. For this act, they underwent a few years of rigorous imprisonment. Then they were enlisted as soldiers in the Second World War, after which they returned to the village, all the more courageous and dashing. At *Panchaya*t meetings they stand up for truth. They never wrong the simple and the in-nocent, nor do they resort to improper means in dealing with anyone, unless they are provoked. They have friends among thieves and gangsters, and hence have a strong force at their beck and call, but they never use this influence against the weak

---

[3] Baniya is the Hindi name of a money-lender.

and unprotected villagers. It is for this reason that they are admired and esteemed in the village, for it is a first-rate quality in a man to have so much power and yet act with restraint and a sense of justice.

(5) P. Singh. He is a young man of about 36, tall, good-looking and healthy, and is a *panch* of the *Gram Sabha*. He is a very prosperous Thakur, owning 30 *Bighas* of land, a few mango and jamun trees, a big house, one buffalo, two cows and two bullocks. He has enough money to give a loan to anyone at any time: yet he leads a simple life, without any pomp or show. He treats all men alike, whether rich or poor, respects the elders and loves the youngsters. He maintains cordial relations with everyone in the village and outside. He is an upright man with a strong sense of justice.

(6) R. Pasi (a *panch* of the *Gram Sabha*). He is the most influential among the Pasis. Judging from the standards of the Pasis, he is economically well off, having a pair of bullocks and a chaff-cutting machine. He does not have to borrow money from anyone, unless some unforeseen mishap befalls him.

R. Pasi is known for his frankness and bold expression of opinions. He is honest and sticks to what he says. He was the last of the Pasis to give up the fight against the Thakurs for the right to wear the *Janeu* (the sacred thread). He can be trusted with any amount of money and any confidential matters. Even the Thakurs give him due respect and the Thakur children address him in terms of kinship. In conversation he is intelligent, good-humoured and well-behaved, though he has a temper which, when kindled, might well prove dangerous.

(7) K. Barhai. Aged 40, he is a *Panch* of the *Gram Sabha*. Economically very well off, he has in his possession 35 *Bighas* of agricultural land, two pairs of bullocks, carts, a cow, two buffaloes, a chaff-cutter and a host of other things, some of which are not owned even by the Thakurs.

Though rich, he is not proud. He helps those in need, and to add to his charm, he helps them secretly. He is good-natured, gentle and honest. Often he is called upon to officiate at the Barhai *Panchayat* held in the absence of the *Chowdhry*, but he never interferes with the affairs of others unless he is asked to take part in them.

Through honoured by the people of his own caste, he never goes against the wishes of the Thakurs; with the result that he is respected in the higher circles also. He often lends his cart and bullocks to the Thakurs. But where there is praise there is blame also. Thus there are some who call K. Barhai a flatterer, and others say that he once tried to seduce a woman when she was alone without any help at hand; but in general he is considered to be intelligent, well-behaved, reliable, peace-loving and honest.

(8) C. Chamar (a *Panch* of the *Gram Sabha*). It appears that he became a *Panch* only because of his permanent support to the Thakurs. The Thakurs say that he is honest and good-natured and some of the Chamars also say so, but there are a few Chamars who criticise him. The fact is that C. Chamar is very particular about pleasing the Thakurs. He is a recognized singer in his community. On the whole, he is regarded by the villagers as an honest, good-natured and uninterfering man. Judged from the standards of Chamars, his economic position is tolerably good.

(9) Dr. M. (A Doctor). He is also an ex-*Zamindar* of the village, and so, when time and circumstances permit, he pays a visit to the village. Though a non-resident of the village, he is quite popular there. When he is in the village, the villagers, children and adults, crowd round him for advice. If one wishes to be admitted to a hospital, Dr. M's help can always be relied upon. But it is not in the medical field alone that he can help the villagers. He is a peace-maker, and the villagers bring their quarrels to him. If police help is necessary, he does the needful to secure it. Further, he makes enquiries about their fields and animals and talks on any subject that would interest the villagers. He has knowledge, wealth, status, power, and above all a genuine interest in the villagers, though he himself lives in the town.

The above study made by Majumdar (1962) has revealed that various factors go to make a man influential in the village. Wealth, age, intelligence, honesty, kindness, renunciation of wealth, being born in high caste and pull with authorities are some of the important factors which make a leader command respect and obedience in the villages. All these qualities are rarely possessed by any leader. Several permutations and combinations of these qualities are found in different leaders. It is a significant fact to note that of the 10 leaders described by Majumdar one is an ex-*Zamindar,* three have some influence among thieves and gangsters and two have influence and connections with the police.

Money and influence count a great deal towards social prestige in the village. Caste also ranks high in the scale of social precedence. The ex-*Zamindar,* if he belongs to a high caste. still has some say in the affairs of the village and enjoys the traditional loyalty in spite of the changed conditions today.

(c) *Classification of villages in relation to leadership*

The progress of adoption of programmes in villages is directly dependent upon the interest taken by the leaders available in them. If the leaders are active, interested and have initiative, the programmes are easily adopted. otherwise they take a long time.

Different villages have different types and number of active leaders. The villages can be classified into three categories from the point of view of leadership available in them. namely:

    (*i*) Leaderless villages
    (*ii*) One-leader villages
    (*iii*) Multi-leader villages

(*i*) *Leaderless villages*

As the term 'leaderless villages' signifies, it means that there are no leaders in such villages. This is not what this term apparently suggests. Some kind of leadership exists in such villages also. but this leadership is inactive, indifferent, unimaginative and not interested in the welfare of the people. It lacks initiative. It is on account of these deficiencies that such villages look as if they have no leaders even though they may have leaders of some kind. In such villages when elections are held for *Panchayats,* co-operative societies, or some other allied organisations, some so-called leaders are elected as office-holders of these institutions as a part of statutory provisions of the law. They are elected because somebody or the other is to be elected to satisfy the provisions of the law. Once

2

the election is over, they show little active interest in development programmes. Such villages, therefore, are as good as if they have no leaders.

Such villages are very difficult to be tackled for extension of new programmes. Before initiating them, they need to be provided with some kind of catalytic spark to rouse their enthusiasm and bring them out of the rut and shake their complacency, if any. The extension worker in such villages has to play the role of a catalyser and to awaken them from their slumber by bringing about a new orientation in their outlook and pointing out new vistas of life which lie ahead. He has to spot out a few people in such villages, convince them about the new programmes by laying out new demonstrations or through study tours and inspire them to assume responsibility for leading the people.

In community development block Pratapgarh in the same district in Uttar Pradesh, there is a *Gram Sabha* known as Patulki. Sri Moti Ram Teli is the *Pradhan* of this *Gram Sabha*. He is a very simple person and of a retiring disposition. He has almost no connection with people outside the village. He neither takes interest nor interferes with any village programme. There are no party factions in this village. Everybody seems busy looking after his work and earning his livelihood peacefully. The extension worker in this village felt great difficulty in initiating new programmes.

There is a co-operative society in this village which has also been lying more or less dormant without any activity worth the name. Sri Harnam Singh is the treasurer of this society. The village worker approached him and laid out a few demonstrations on his holding. This convinced him of the efficacy of the improved practices and made him interested in them. Being himself initiated and convinced, he now started taking interest in getting the demonstrated practices adopted by the other farmers also in his village. This started the ball rolling and it gathered momentum. Sri Harnam Singh is now not only helping to improve his village, but he has also now set an example to the neighbouring villages to adopt these improved methods. He is now an active leader of the village.

(*ii*)   *One-leader villages*

There are two types of leaders in these villages:

(1) Elected leaders.

(2) Non-elected leaders as teachers, priests, doctors (*Vaids* or *Hakims*), etc.

(1)   *Elected leaders*:

These leaders are elected by majority vote almost unanimously on account of their ability, integrity and quality of leadership. The people owe explicit allegiance to them. It is due to this quality that they lead and guide the villages of which they are the undisputed leaders.

In Pratapgarh block of the same district in Uttar Pradesh, there is a *Gram Sabha* Seepahimahari. It is 10 miles from the block headquarters. Seventy-five per cent of its population consists of Rajputs. They were mostly small *zamindars* before. After the abolition of the *Zamindari* they started their own cultivation with the help of hired labour. Sri Sitla Prasad Singh has been the *Pradhan* of this *Gram Sabha*. He was an old man, and therefore, he did not take much interest in development work. He continued to be the *Pradhan* upto 1950, after which the village people requested Sri Mata Prasad Singh, *Up-Pradhan* to take over the charge of *Pradhanship*. As soon as Sri Mata Prasad Singh took over charge, the fate of the village came to be unfolded. Immediately after taking over charge he started getting a 2-mile road running from Prithviganj — a market place — to the *Gram Sabha* constructed. He only partially succeeded in this mission. In 1955, he got a *Panchayatghar* constructed with the help of grant-in-aid received from the block.

In 1955, Sri Mata Prasad Singh was again elected Chairman without any contest. Immediately after re-election he established contacts with the block authorities and with their help got the incomplete road completed. A *Gram Sahayak* camp was organised in this village in connection with the *Kharif* and *Rabi* food production drives. The village under the leadership of the *Pradhan* co-operated with the village level worker and succeeded in making these drives a success. The village also

constructed five culverts on the new road. A primary school
was opened as the people felt that their children had to go long
distances in the absence of a school in the village. The *Gram
Sabha* is now itself running this school in which about 50 children are reading. All the drinking water wells were repaired and
five new irrigation wells were constructed. The *Gram Sabha* also
put up a community hand pump, a bath room and a latrine
near the *Panchayatghar*.

A 1.2-mile piece of *kutcha* road leading to the village is now
being made *pucca*. More than 50 masonry compost pits have
been dug for storing refuse and preparing compost. A children's play centre has also now been established. Improved
agricultural implements such as soil turning ploughs, Singh
patellas (planks) and dibblers are now commonly being used by
the farmers. A youth club has also been started. Most of the
crops are now being sown in lines. Green manuring has now
come to be a common practice. The result of all these efforts
was that the *Gram Sabha* stood first in the block in *Kharif*
and *Rabi* Campaigns, 1959-60. The successful *Rabi* and
Kharif Campaigns in the *Gram Sabha* brought into light 3 new
village leaders, namely Sri Uma Shanker Singh, Sri Ram Pal
Singh and Sri Suresh Singh, who guide other cultivators from
time to time. Of them, Sri Ram Pal Singh is the oldest—about
60 years of age. He used to oppose the idea of sowing crops
in lines. He is now the most enthusiastic supporter and sows
his entire crops in lines and also persuades others to do so.

All the progress made by this *Gram Sabha* has been due
to the untiring energy and influence of Sri Mata Prasad Singh,
the *Pradhan* who is an undisputed leader of the village. His
influence is now not only limited to his village but also to the
neighbouring villages of Bhagsaera, Pooranpur and Naubasta.
His efforts to construct the 2-mile road previously mentioned
contributed to his popularity and reputation in the neighbouring villages as this road proved to be a boon for them also.

In Paraspur block of Gonda district (Uttar Pradesh), there
was an epidemic of Haemorrhagic Septicaemia affecting the cattle.
As soon as the Block Development Officer got knowledge of it,
he started giving prophylactic vaccinations against Haemorrhagic
Septicaemia to the cattle. The Village Level Workers succeeded

in their mission except in *Gram Sabha* Tulsipur where an important person of the locality resided. He did not favour the idea of vaccination and on account of him, nobody in the village consented to get his cattle vaccinated. He was the undisputed leader of the village, and therefore, people depended on his lead. Hearing about his resistance, the Block Development Officer and Assistant Development Officer concerned approached him and requested him to get his cattle vaccinated against the disease. He somehow yielded to the pressure. The news immediately went round and from the next day others followed suit.

The above are typical examples of how sometimes the leaders in the villages affect the adoption of programmes. The problem becomes simpler if the leaders in such villages are convinced and won over.

(2) *Non-elected leaders*:

These leaders are not very much interested in holding any office. They are either priests, doctors, money lenders or some other specialized persons.

In *Gram Sabha* Kopa of Pratapgarh block of the same district in Uttar Pradesh, the leadership is concentrated in Sri Mathura Dutt Shastri. He is a priest of the village as well as of neighbouring ones consisting of a large population of *Kshetrias.* He is respected by almost the entire population of these villages. The area of this *Gram Sabha* is about 350 acres and is subject to severe erosion.

Shastriji has been an ardent supporter of the programmes launched by the official agencies. He has the habit of attending all village meetings and takes an active part in them. The Village Level Workers of the area persuaded Shastriji to sow a small area of his wheat by dibbling. He got an yield of 4 maunds (about 40 maunds per acre) from this small plot of 2 *Biswas*. This woke up the sleeping giant spirit in him and converted him to be the greatest votary of improved agricultural practices. He himself started experimenting with new things. There was no paddy area in this village. Shastriji started sowing paddy in one of his fields according to the Japanese method recommended to him by the Village Level

Worker. He got an yield of 15 maunds (about 45 maunds per acre) from this plot. This convinced him further of the benefits of improved practices. He then started propagating the new practices amongst his clients besides carrying out his profession of priesthood. Later on he got constructed a 2-mile *Shramdan* road and one *Panchayatghar* and started a youth club in the *Gram Sabha*.

Shastriji's interest in the improvement of the village continued to increase by leaps and bounds. He started with the help of the block workers soil conservation measures in about 250-acres area of the village, and got two masonry *bandhies* constructed, one of which involved an expenditure of Rs. 5,000/- for a span of 40 feet. His initiative in this programme was very much liked by the authorities of the Agriculture Department who later on selected this area for a Central Government project on dry farming. Not only Kopa *Gram Sabha* was included in this project, but also the neighbouring *Gram Sabhas* of Rajgarh, Sree Nathpur, Naubasta, Bahalpur and Dagencha. Shastriji is now not only the priest of these villages, but also their undisputed leader.

In Qasimabad block of Ghazipur district in Uttar Pradesh there is a *Gram Sabha*, Deoli. There is a tank in this *Gram Sabha*. It is used for irrigation as well as for drinking water by the cattle. The project authorities selected this tank for deepening it during the *Shramdan* drive in 1952. The village level worker approached the people but they did not respond favourably. The reason for this indifference was investigated and it was found that the official leaders of the *Gram Sabha* and the *Panchayat* were not the real leaders of the village. The real leader was Pandit Ram Prakash. He was a good agriculturist and commanded respect of all, but he never cared to aspire for any office or to come in the lime light. He was even shy to meet government officials. He was, however, a very bold and frank speaker in village meetings. The Assistant Development Officer (Agriculture) who was incharge of the project called a meeting of the *Gram Sabha* and ensured his presence also. He successfully persuaded all those who were recalcitrant with the result that they came to offer their *Shramdan* the next day.

The *Nyaya Panchayat Sarpanch* of the area belonged to this village. He exercised great influence on the *Pradhan* who belonged to his party. The *Sarpanch* sometime back was reported to have misappropriated Rs. 80/- received from the sale of fish from this very tank. All the Harijans of this village were therefore, very much annoyed with him and were opposed to the idea of *Shramdan* for they neither got fish nor money for their *Shramdan*. Prior to the opening of the block in the area, a sum of Rs. 32/- was collected from the people for deepening this tank. This money was misappropriated by another *Panch* of the neighbouring village who was a friend of the *Sarpanch*. Nobody dared speak the truth for fear. The truth came out in the above meeting and as the result both the *Sarpanch* and the *Panch* had to deposit the money. Some breakfast and *Sharbat* (sugar-water) was arranged with this money the next morning. The *Shramdan* which was not being offered due to dishonesty of leaders was now in full swing. The tank was deepened. It proved to be of immense value to the people.

The success in the case was due to the frank and bold talk and stand taken in the meeting by Pandit Ram Prakash who was the natural leader of the people and was respected by them for integrity and selflessness. His quality of renunciation in not trying to seek an office in the village was his greatest asset which the people valued.

(iii) *Multi-leader villages*

The multi-leader villages are generally of two types:

(1) Those in which leadership is divided on some family or election rivalry or feud.

(2) Those in which leadership is divided on some religious, social or economic factors.

The extension worker in multi-leader villages has to act as a bridge between the faction leaders and bring them together on some common platform or agreement for the good of the community. His role in this respect has to be very polite, cautious and diplomatic. He is not to align himself with any group but act in a way that each group considers him to be their friend and well wisher. In course of time, if the factions feel that the extension worker is impartial and he has nothing but the good of the community in his heart they would unconsciously be coming together with the passing of time on account of the healing role of the extension worker.

Healing touch of the extension worker many a time is found to convert warring factions into constructive groups with their separate identity in many cases remaining intact. The speed of adoption of programmes in such villages becomes faster on account of competition and healthy rivalry. In Bhoopiamau *Gram Sabha* of Pratapgarh block of the same district (Uttar Pradesh), there were two caste factions—one belonging to Brahmins and the other to *Kshetrias*. The population of Brahmins was less than that of the *Kshetrias*. Even within the *Kshetrias* there were several sub-factions. The Village Level Worker on account of the factions did not contact any prominent leader of the groups, but contacted Sri Ramanand Dubey who was an ordinary cultivator. His economic condition was not good. The Village Level Worker laid out a few demonstrations of improved practices on his land. He was convinced about them and in subsequent years increased his production and income to an appreciable extent. Seeing his production increasing, some other farmers joined him in adopting the same improved practices and also started coming to the Village Level Worker for advice and guidance. Sri Narsingh Bahadur, School Teacher and Sri Majadev Singh, who belonged to the *Kshetri* faction were its prominent leaders. They also started showing interest and adopted new practices. Seeing them adopting new practices, other members of this faction followed suit. The same process started in the other faction consisting of Brahmins. The condition in this *Gram Sabha* now is that there is always a keen competition between the two factions as to who adopts the new practices earlier and in a larger area. The village, in spite of the factions, is now on the road to progress.

As against the above *Gram Sabha*, there is another *Gram Sabha*, named Gonda in the same State which has not yet reacted favourably to the healing touch of the Village Level Worker. The population of this village is about 2,500 consisting of about 400 families. Out of 400 families, 250 families belong to *Kshetri*

caste alone. Most of the families were originally small *Zamindars,* but now they are farmers like others. This *Gram Sabha* did not previously have any recognised factions, but they started growing when the *Panchayat* election came nearer in 1955-56.

Sri M. Singh was the *Pradhan* of the *Gram Sabha* prior to the election. He co-operated well with the Village Level Worker and helped to establish a community orchard in the *Gram Sabha* with the help of the block authorities who granted a subsidy of Rs. 1,000/-. The village showed a keen interest in socio-cultural activities also and won several prizes for their performance from the block.

Some people in the village did not like the growing popularity of Sri M. Singh and they, therefore, started putting obstacles in his way. A few persons, out of jealousy damaged the community orchard and started grazing their cattle in the orchard. The *Panchayat* election took place in 1956-57. In this election, one Shri Y. Singh of Sri M. Singh's party was elected as the *Pradhan* of the *Gram Sabha.* Sri Z. Singh who was a pleader in the city but belonged to this village filed an election petition against Sri Y. Singh. This aggravated the rivalry. Now the entire village instead of thinking of constructive programmes started fighting over petty matters. They even quarrelled over the prizes the *Gram Sabha* won when Sri H. Singh was the *Pradhan.*

Sri M. Singh who was sometime back a leader of the village became a party man. He developed a desire to seek revenge from his rivals. He even tried to get the land under community orchard which was planted when he was the *Pradhan,* transferred to the name of his son. He did not succeed in this mission and later on died. The election petition which was filed sometime back by Sri Z. Singh against Sri Y. Singh was declared valid and thus Sri Y. Singh lost his presidentship. After this, Sri A. Singh of the opposite party was elected as the new *Pradhan* in January 1959. This further aggravated the tension and rivalry in the village intensifying the party feuds and further bedevilling the village situation.

During the Presidentship of Sri M. Singh, the village got a prize of some musical instrument from the rural development authorities. Sri A. Singh, the new *Pradhan* and his men sold these instruments and misappropriated the money. The other party immediately reported the matter to the police who took them to task. This aggravated the rivalry.

The village is now the hot-bed of politics and rivalry. Nobody now thinks of improving the village. The common talk in the village is as to what the other is doing or has done and how to take revenge.

The extension agency is now in a fix as to how to bring about a change in the situation. The Village Level Worker has now started contacting a few non-party farmers hoping to build them up as future constructive leaders.

The case histories given above in connection with the classification of villages from the point of view of leadership indicate that extension of programmes is interlinked to a great extent with the leadership available in the villages. Successful programmes can create new leaders, build the sleeping and inactive ones and encourage and enthuse the existing ones. Similarly, the leaders exercise great influence upon programmes. They can make a success of the programme or make it a failure. They can lead the villages to perpetual strife or rivalry, ruining them, their followers and their own selves completely. They can also lead them to prosperity by changing their thinking and values in life. Such is the relationship between leaders and programmes. In view of this close relationship, the extension worker is advised to make a detailed study of the village leadership before starting a programme and then plan his methods of approaching people accordingly. Within wider limits, the problem of extension consists of tackling and handling people. If it is so, the people should be studied first before initiating any programme among them. This aspect is being very much neglected at present in our Community Development and Agricultural Programmes. The worker needs to be better trained in this art of handling people. The sooner it is done, the better it would be and these programmes would gain sound footing from the social, cultural, psychological and emotional point of view.

(d) Contacting leaders in different types of villages

The villages have been classified above according to the types of leadership available in them, into 3 categories, namely, leaderless villages, one-leader villages and multi-leader villages. Each type of village presents different problems. It is, therefore, necessary to tackle them differently.

(i) Leaderless villages

The elected leader or some potential leader in such villages has to be contacted, convinced through discussions, study tours, demonstrations, *etc.* and activitised. The selection of the potential leader should be done very carefully for ultimate success of the programme would greatly depend upon his selection.

(ii) One-leader villages

The problem in such villages is very simple, for their leaders are known. They are simply required to be convinced and enthused by the usual extension methods for adopting the recommended programmes.

(iii) Multi-leader villages

These villages present the toughest problem to the extension worker. The usual method followed in these villages is either to contact the elected leaders or a few individuals on *ad hoc* basis. Contacting the elected leader, more generally the *Pradhan* of the *Gram Sabha,* convincing him and then expecting him to convince others and to help in the extension of programmes is very often too much to expect when the society is divided into several castes and factions. It is not that success cannot at all be obtained by this method, but the chances of success of this method are generally very remote. The success in most of such cases is very much delayed and more often wrecked or lost on the rock of group factions, rivalries or caste prejudices.

The approach of contacting the *Pradhan* is in keeping with the times to make *Panchayats* the fulcrum of all development activities in the villages. Contacting the *Pradhan* alone and depending upon him for the execution of the programme is very often quite risky in situations where the *Pradhan* is a party or a faction man. Programmes do not go ahead in such cases due to group or personal jealousies or rivalries. This situation arises in those cases also where the *Pradhan* belongs to a low caste group because the high caste groups which are generally very resourceful and rich and possess a major portion of the village land, do not like to co-operate with him on grounds of caste prejudices. Such *Pradhans* have been found to do very well in programmes like *Shramdan* in which the low caste people generally play a major part. Success in the items like *Shramdan* in the case of *Pradhans* belonging to low caste groups becomes more or less a prestige issue for the *Pradhan*.

Working only or primarily through the official head of a village has also been found to be not a sound policy in a study carried out by Lewis Oscar[4] (1954) in India. This study has revealed that if one only followed the method of contacting the *Pradhan* in the village, one would find it difficult to communicate with all the villagers and even worse it might estrange a large portion of the villagers.

As against approaching the elected leaders, the other approach of contacting *ad hoc* individuals is also not free from defects. By this method also programmes do not catch roots. Individuals selected on *ad hoc* basis for trying the programme and then getting it accepted by others, do not generally represent the entire cross-section of the people. They are more often opportunist persons working for their own personal ends rather than for the good of the community or village. They, therefore, do not act as good communicators of the programme and motivators in the community village.

The proper approach in such villages appears to be not only to contact the elected leader but also other faction leaders, for neither of them can be ignored. The details of this method of approach are outlined below step by step:

(1) The extension workers should first contact the *Pradhan* of the *Panchayat* for initiating any new item of development work in consultation with the people.

(2) He should then slowly and slowly study and identify all group or faction leaders and approach them individually for initiating and educating them in the programme under question.

---

[4] Oscar Lewis (1954)—*Group dynamics in a North Indian village*, Programme Evaluation Organization, Planning Commission, New Delhi.

(3) He should arrange a meeting of all those group or faction leaders and bring them to have a common understanding. Such meetings may in the beginning be a sort of failure, but if the approach of the extension worker is correct and impartial, he would ultimately succeed after some common-ground for agreement has been found out.

(4) Besides the group leaders, he should also contact and convince a few important persons of each group. It has been noticed that in the majority of the cases the decision does not always lie with the leaders themselves. Besides them there are also a few other key persons who guide the thinking of the group and the leaders themselves. Such persons are also necessary to be contacted and tackled to mobilise the group.

(5) The programme should then be carried out with the help of all these individuals *i.e.*, *Pradhan,* group leaders, decision makers and one or two other good persons who may neither be leaders nor decision makers, but may have some kind of good reputation in the village.

The advantages of such an approach to our extension problems are as follows:

(*i*) It takes into account the existing traditional group, factional, caste or kinship leaderships into confidence and tries to bring them together reducing factionalism in the village and infusing a spirit of co-operation, joint effort and deliberations for the common goal of improving the village.

(*ii*) It takes into account the elected leadership mainly, the *Pradhan* of the *Panchayat* into confidence for all the developmental activities planned to be carried out through the *Panchayats*. Even though the approach through the *Pradhan* may not be always effective, yet it is felt necessary to give weight to his position and to the organisation he represents. This is only by strengthening the institutions and its leaders that it would be possible to create some life into them.

(*iii*) It is possible to utilise the group and faction leaders to convey new ideas to the members of their groups earlier than through neutral or *ad hoc* individuals or by contacting the *Pradhan*. Such leaders provide ready made communication channels to the people. If the extension worker communicates even with only a single member of each faction, he will be able to convey his message to most of the families of the village.

(*iv*) It would make it possible to spot out and build leaders in technical fields who if encouraged would be able to replace the old leadership by bringing to the surface points of common social and economic interests of the community as a whole. Encouraging and building such leaders is expected in the long run to reduce factional bickerings and caste, and social prejudices also.

(*v*) It would bring to light the common objective for which different groups within the community should strive separately and also jointly.

What the extension worker would have to do is to educate the leaders of different groups within the community and create in them a desire to change.

(*vi*) It would provide for a much closer representation of the people than is possible in the monolithic type of political democracy based on delegated authority. It will enable the worker successfully to change the hostility between the groups into a healthy rivalry for constructive aims.

The method of approach outlined above is likely to succeed only if the extension worker works with complete impartiality and independence and has a wide sympathy for their common problems and helps to solve them.

The recent innovation of *Gram Sahayak* (village leaders) training started by the Ministry of Community Development and Co-operation, Government of India in 1958-59 was a step forward in the adoption of the above approach, but the method of selection of the *Gram Sahayaks* followed was such that it did not evoke as much enthusiasm as was expected. Their selection was mainly done by the extension workers on *ad hoc* basis or with the help of the *Gram Sabha*. The persons selected were either those who belonged to the majority party or were self-appointed or opportunist leaders or those who were useless at home and to the village.

The selection of *Gram Sahayaks* in *Gram Sabha* meetings meant selection of all those who belonged to the party of the *Pradhan*. The meetings in which the selections were made were generally not represented by all the sections of the population and were mostly attended by the party men of the *Pradhan* or other interested persons. This method of selection did not throw up real and representative leadership.

Although the institution of the *Gram Sahayak* is making its effects felt in the villages, yet they would have been more effective if their selection was made on group basis along with the selection of those who possessed some special technical skill or desire to work for the good of the village. The idea is to work through the existing social, cultural, economic groupings and lead them slowly and slowly on the road to new technological, cultural and social development. The existing leadership cannot be ignored. It has to be taken into account to start with but with the clear aim of evolving a new functional leadership in which the new as well as the old leaders start thinking more and more on constructive issues.

4. *Successful running of the people's institutions*

Of the peoples institutions, *Panchayats* and Co-operatives are the two important institutions which help a great deal in furthering the extension of programmes good for the people. They serve as a base around which all activities are weaved and ensure continuity of the programmes.

Peoples' institutions being an important part of the people themselves are necessary to be run efficiently for becoming useful to them. Several factors go to make for their success. The Programme Evaluation Organisation of the Planning Commission carried out a study of the 20 selected *Panchayats* and co-operatives in the country in 1959-60 and published a report giving details of how success was obtained by each of these institutions. The selection of the institutions was carried out by the heads of the departments of the concerned States. Of the 20 institutions selected, studies in respect of 4 institutions were dropped on account of insufficient data. Of the remaining 16, full details were also not available in respect of two institutions. Thus fourteen institutions (8 *Panchayats* and 6 co-operatives) remained, of which full details were available. Below is given a list of the important factors which led to the success of these individual institutions. After describing the factors which led to the success of the individual institutions of each type, a summary has been given of the factors which led to the success of the two types of institutions in general:

(A) *Panchayats*

(i) *Noorsarai Panchayat, Bihar Sharif (Bihar)*

(*a*) Quality of *Mukhia* President. (*b*) Indirect procedure of election to the *Panchayat*. (*c*) The growing Bazar (market).

The rapid growth of Noorsarai Bazar has been able to raise the income of the people in the village and therefore, the response of the people to the programme has been better.

(*d*) Compactness of the area and social cohesion among the various sections of community. (*e*) Typical caste and occupation pattern and absence of factions. (*f*) Influence of traditional *Panchayat*. (*g*) Influence of the external agencies like the block and pilot project for industries.

(ii) *Rangwasa Panchayat—District Indore (Madhya Pradesh)*

(*a*) Proper leadership. (*b*) Internal harmony and team spirit. (*c*) Building up outside contact which helped to mobilise support for its activities. (*d*) Expansion of resources especially for non-tax sources. (*e*) People's response both in the form of money and labour. (*f*) Proximity of Rangwasa to Indore. (*g*) Congenial caste composition. (*h*) Developing village economy.

(iii) *Ramanathapur Panchayat, Hassan (Mysore)*

(*a*) Harmonious relationship between the various minor and major castes. (*b*) Selfless and progressive leadership. (*c*) Guidance from officials.

(iv) *Khawaja Nangla Panchayat—District Meerut (Uttar Pradesh).*

(*a*) Enlightened and devoted leadership. (*b*) Strength of character of the people. (*c*) Economic prosperity.

There is considerable economic prosperity in the village and this has made a material contribution to the cause of village improvement. The foremost among the conditions making for economic prosperity is the cultivation of sugarcane on a wide scale and for a long time.

(*d*) Communication with towns.   (*e*) Personal examples of the leaders themselves.

The leaders of the campaign not only preached but also practised what they preached.   They were the first to construct compost pits for depositing cattle dung and refuse, start pavement of streets before their own houses and make cash contribution as well as *Shramdan* before asking others to do so.   Their gospel went by both practice and precept.   It gained a ready ear from the people who got a fairly good understanding of what they were expected to do to bring about an improvement in their lives.

(*f*)   Organisational efficiency.

The *Panchayat* has displayed considerable organisational efficiency in executing works.   It did not entrust any work to a contractor, but executed them all itself.

The supervision of all the jobs was exercised by the *Panchayat*. For the pavement of streets, it divided the work according to localities, selected a leading man from each locality and made him responsible for getting the work executed.   This worked very well.   For other works, such as the school building, *Panchayatghar,* bus shelters, embankment of village tanks, *etc.,* the *Panchayat* itself organised the work by placing each such work in charge of one or more of its members, co-opting other influential persons of the village and mobilising participation from the people in one form or the other.

(*g*) Governmental assistance.

(*v*)   *Tehta village Panchayat—District Gaya (Bihar)*

(*a*) Harmony in village.   (*b*) Enlightened leadership.   (*c*) Good *Panchayat* Secretary.   (*d*) Easy accessibility of the village by rail and road.   (*e*) Growing prosperity of the village.

A sub-Mandi has developed in the village.

(*vi*) *Kayadra village Panchayat—District Junagadh (Gujarat)*

(*a*) People have national outlook and spirit of public service due to their association with Gandhiji and the Indian

3

National Congress. (*b*) Existence of institutions like Saurashtra Rachnatamak Samiti, the Saurashtra Kharif Gram Udyog Mandal, The Harijan Sewak Samaj, Keshod Mahal Vikas Mandal, *etc.* who are implementing the constructive programme of the Congress. (*c*) Absence of political factions. (*d*) Amicable social relations between the important caste groups. (*e*) Enlightened leadership and presence of selfless workers. (*f*) Active association of the ex-Development Minister of Saurashtra with the village. (*g*) Keen interest taken by the Manavadar-Vanthali Keshod Community Project. (*h*) Benevolent attitude of the Government to the *Panchayat*. (*i*) Villagers' readiness to work hard for achieving economic prosperity and social amity.

(*vii*) *Village   Panchayat—Paganeri,   District   Ramanathpuram* (*Madras*)

(*a*) Influential leadership.

The *Panchayat* had the benefit of some mature advice and guidance of some influential leaders. The rich individuals of the village have a philanthropic bent of mind. They made large contributions to the *Panchayat* for undertaking some development works in the village.

(*b*) Benevolent Influence of communal bodies.

Various bodies in the village have laid down a healthy convention to avoid contest in the election to the *Panchayat*.

(*c*) Momentum of an early start. (*d*) Assistance from the blocks.

(*viii*) *Tirga Panchayat—District Durg—*(*Madhya Pradesh*)

(a) Emergence of a band of volunteers in the village. (*b*) Collaboration of the traditional leadership with the new leadership. (*c*) Unity and absence of social tension. (*d*) *Ad hoc* contributions from the village and *Sarpanch's* family.

Summarising the factors which led to the success of the individual *Panchayats,* eight factors appeared important and necessary for their success. All these eight factors were not common to the success of all the *Panchayats*. They varied to some extent but in general, they can be said to be mainly responsible for the success of the *Panchayats*.

(i) *Honest and enlightened leadership*

This has been one of the most important factors for the suc-cess of the *Panchayats*. The qualities of leadership that helped were:

(a) Honesty, conscientiousness, straightforwardness, zeal and enthusiasm. (b) Progressiveness. (c) Ability to organise and inspire confidence among the people by working with devotion and in a democratic manner. (d) Sparing sufficient time to the work of the *Panchayat*. (e) Personal examples of leaders them-selves. (f) Benevolent attitude and readiness to donate funds themselves (in some cases).

(ii) *New leadership working with traditional leadership*

The traditional leadership is slow to work and less prone to new ideas. It has deep roots in the villages and the people. It derives its strength from the *status quo* and therefore, it makes persistent efforts to maintain it. Unless the new leaders ack-nowledge them as leaders they come in direct conflict with them. The task of the new leaders becomes easier if the traditional leaders co-operate with them in the organisation of new activi-ties. Working through traditional leadership to start with helps one to avoid tension and friction between them and the new lead-ers making the working of the institutions smooth. The proce-dure also helps in course of time to throw out the traditional leadership and to replace it with the new progressive leadership.

(iii) *Internal harmony and team spirit in the people and their leaders*

Internal harmony and team spirit depends upon:

(a) Relationship between different castes and traditional groups. (b) Results and procedure of election.

Institutions which have unanimous elections or undivided leadership succeed better in their programmes than others. Ins-titutions with divided leadership remain a house divided with no clear cut policy and continuity of programme.

In Noorsarai *Panchayat* of Bihar Sharif (Bihar) mentioned above, there is an altogether different procedure of election to the *Panchayat*. Before the regular election to the statutory

Panchayat, the traditional *Panchayat* calls an informal meeting of all the adults of the village for electing the persons. Whoever is elected in this meeting, files a nomination paper for the formal and official election. The real election is held at the informal meeting where the people get a free hand to choose their *Panchayat.* They make their choice through unanimity of their opinion. This procedure has saved the community from contests and from a consequent wastage of energy in electioneering. The idea of giving this example is not to create the impression that we must establish traditional *Panchayats* wherever they are not there, but to emphasize that as far as possible attempt has to be made to ensure unanimous elections.

(c) Absence of factions and feuds.

Factions and feuds are the worst stumbling factors which cause hindrance to the working of *Panchayats.* The extension workers who constantly endeavour to reduce and discourage them by making them agree on some common platform or programme, help a great deal in smooth running of the institutions.

(iv) People's response in the form of money and labour

This depends upon the economic condition and general awareness of the people. Better the response from the people, better and quicker is the execution of programmes launched by the *Panchayats.* In view of the fact that the people's response is better where they are economically better, it is necessary for each *Panchayat* to initiate programmes which improve the economic condition of the people.

(v) Development of own resources through proper management

The *Panchayats* which try to develop their own additional resources besides levying direct taxes, are in a better position to work than others which entirely depend for their income on direct taxes. Some of the important items through which the *Panchayats* can increase their income are:

(a) Development of *Gram Panchayat* land to yield permanent income. (b) Development of fisheries in *Panchayat* ponds and tanks, if any. (c) Establishment of markets, cattle fairs, *etc.* (d) Establishment of industries. (e) Taking up labour contracts for works (*f*) Organising cultural shows. (*g*) Exploitation of natural resources as quarries, forests, *etc*.

(*vi*) *Help and guidance from external agencies like*

(*a*) Government and its staff. (*b*) Non-official workers, leaders and institutions.

Much depends upon the help and guidance received by the *Panchayats* from the external agencies. Where the guidance and help is timely, purposeful and continuous, the people are led from inactivity to activity, from confusion to order and from fatalism to longing for progress. Guidance and help to be effective are to be continuous and not sporadic.

Government, its staff and non-official constructive workers have a great responsibility to shoulder in this respect for their attitude and behaviour towards the institution can go a long way in jeopardizing or ensuring its success.

(*vii*) *Good management*

(*a*) Timely tax realization and its proper utilisation for items of common good. (*b*) Impartial dealings. (*c*) Efficient *Panchayat* secretary. (*d*) Availability of time with the *Pradhan* for *Panchayat* work. (*e*) Building up of the resources of the *Panchayat*.

Efficient management of a *Panchayat* is closely associated with the above 5 factors (*a, b, c, d* and *e*). If they are ensured, success is almost a certainty.

(*viii*) *Good location—Easy accessibility*

(*a*) Nearness to road. (*b*) Nearness to Railway Station. (*c*) Nearness to some industrial or other economic or constructive institutions.

All these count a great deal in the successful running of the *Panchayat* for general prosperity of the village depends to a great extent upon these factors. If these factors are not there, the *Panchayat* should strive for and get them established through its own or external resources. It has been seen that many a time even the construction of an approach road leads the village *Panchayat* to better economic prosperity of its people.

(B) *Co-operatives*

(*i*) *Rukadi Co-operative Society—District Kolhapur (Maharashtra)*

(*a*) Influence of co-operative movement in the district. (*b*) Emphasis on owned capital. (*c*) Business instinct of the Jain community the members of which were the sponsors of the society. (*d*) Maintenance of unity by the leaders. (*e*) Maintenance of good relationship with the officials of the Central Bank and other influential persons.

(*ii*) *Jassia Agricultural Service Co-operative Society—District Rohtak (Punjab)*

(*a*) Devoted leadership. (*b*) General prosperity of the village. (*c*) Timely guidance from departmental officers.

(*iii*) *Shri Jaganmohna Ranganathaswamy Co-operative Society Ltd., Belkavadi—District Mandya (Mysore)*

(*a*) Enthusiasm of the chief promoter. (*b*) Disinterested service of its honorary secretary. (*c*) Its location near the hydroelectric station. (*d*) Training of members of the managing committee. (*e*) Employment of paid staff. (*f*) Personal sincerity and integrity of its leaders.

(*iv*) *Kursanda Co-operative Society—Mathura District (Uttar Pradesh)*

(*a*) Harmony in the village. (*b*) Good members of the Managing Committee. (*c*) Financial stability. (*d*) Paid workers of the Society. (*e*) Good-will of the people for the society. (*f*) Impartiality in dealings.

(*v*) *Athaula Large-sized Co-operative Society, Jullundher (Punjab).*

(*a*) Absence of factions and feuds. (*b*) Good management. (*c*) Fulfilment of credit requirement in time. (*d*) General prosperity of the village. (*e*) Presence of an honest and wholetime Secretary. (*f*) Government participation in the share capital. (*g*) Conversion of the society into a large-sized society.

(vi) *Mallasamudram Co-operative Society, Salem (Madras)*

(a) Easy accessibility to important towns. (b) Concentration of different livelihood classes in different areas. (c) The general co-operative spirit in the area. (d) Non-interference by the leaders in the society's affairs. (e) Management of the society. (f) Multiple activities of the society. (g) Raising of large deposits. (h) Offering of special loans by the society as Jewel loans, chit funds, *etc.*

Summarising the factors which led to the success of the above 6 co-operatives, eight factors looked significant and necessary for their success. All these factors were not common to all the co-operatives. As in the case of *Panchayats,* they varied to some extent but in general they can be said to be mainly responsible for the success of the co-operatives. These factors were:

(i) *Good management*

(a) Impartial dealings and tendency to serve the people. (b) Fulfilment of credit requirement in time. (c) Emphasis on development of own resources in the form of its own paid up capital and reserve funds.

(In one society, the leaders deducted 10% as a rule from all loans advanced as contribution to the share capital. This helped to build up the capital of the society. The strong base of owned capital enabled the society to expand its credit and service functions to a great extent. Deducting a certain percentage from loans as a compulsory deposit or saving is, in fact, a very sound principle of co-operation commonly practised in the United States of America, Canada and even in a few parts of India with great success.)

(d) Financial stability. (e) Ensuring full realisations of dues.

Good management is the most important key to the success of a co-operative society. Good management is almost synonymous with the five important factors (a) to (e) given above.

(ii) *Employment of paid workers and staff*

This is essential for the success of any institution. It ensures proper and continuous supervision. Those institutions which do

not keep a whole-time or part-time paid staff and are run on
the good-will of somebody generally go mismanaged because the
generous donor of time gives first priority to his own work and
second priority to the work of the society. Every programme
has its own time and if the proper time is lost, it does not come
back.

(iii) *Timely and proper guidance from departmental personnel*

This is specially necessary under our conditions because the
institutions are small and manned by illiterate or semi-literate
people who do not have proper knowledge of rules and regulations and lack initiative and methodology.

(iv) *Absence of feuds and factions*

(*a*) Harmony in the village.   (*b*) Good-will of the people for
the institution.

Feuds and factions damage the working of the institutions.
Attempts have to be made to arrive at agreed solutions. Usually
failure at the elections and later on favouritism by the leaders
of the majority party to members of their own party are common causes of party feelings in the institutions. The official
machinery can play a great part in reducing differences provided
it is alive to the problem and constantly endeavours to bring
the factions together.

(v) *Sincere and honest leadership*

Proper running of the co-operative societies depends to a great
extent upon the interest taken by the leaders in these institutions,
upon their attitude and behaviour with the members and upon
their personal character.

(vi) *Government participation in the share capital of the society*

It helps to stabilise the economic condition of the society,
creates confidence in the members and increases its borrowing
capacity and volume of business. The factor of Government
participation becomes all the more important because these institutions are generally very small in size and cannot stand on
their own legs unless helped.

(vii) *General economic condition of the people*

The interest taken by the members in the society is generally very much dependent upon the general economic condition of its members. Better the economic condition of the members, better the realisation of dues and deposits in the society.

All the seven factors above, which are expected to contribute to the success of the co-operatives, should as far as possible be helped to be created if they are not there. Much depends in this respect upon the attitude and approach of the machinery supervising the programme.

5. *Mass Action*

Mass action to adopt the programmes is possible only when the people are properly aroused to understand their responsibility and to realize what is good for them. Executive orders have no meaning unless people have been properly educated, trained and aroused. Many workers think that they have done their job if they have been able to think of the situation and issue executive orders for compliance by their subordinates or by the people. Many of the evils of the present day extension programmes are due to this attitude of workers who in good number of cases are themselves quite divorced from the field.

That pre-education, initiation and arousing the people as a prelude to mass action for the benefit of the village/community/country is a great need and a *must* is not only believed by all the democratic governments, but also by the totalitarian and communist governments like that of China and Russia.

"We launched the movement for agricultural co-operation on the basis of a thoroughly completed land reform", states Liu Shao Ch'i,[5] "In carrying out the land reform our Party did not take the simple and easy way of merely relying on administrative decrees and of 'bestowing' land on the peasants. For three solid years after the establishment of the People's Republic of China, we applied ourselves to awakening the class consciousness of the peasants... we consider the time spent was absolutely

[5] From the Political report of the Central Committee of the Communist Party of China submitted to the Eighth National Congress of the Party, September 15th, 1956.

necessary. Because we had used such a method, the peasant masses stood up on their own feet, got themselves organised, closely followed the lead of the Communist Party and the People's Government, and took the reins of government and the armed forces in the villages firmly into their hands. The broad masses of the awakened peasants held that exploitation, whether by landlords or by rich peasants was a shameful thing. Conditions were thus created which were favourable to the subsequent socialist transformation of agriculture and helped shorten to a great extent the time needed to bring about agricultural co-operation."

This method of approach for mobilising mass action has been called by the Chinese Communist as the 'Mass Line approach' and is conceived to be based on four concepts which must be firmly established in the mind of every Party member for pursuing it effectively. These four concepts as described by Liu Shao Ch'i are:

"Firstly, there is the standpoint that everything is for the masses and for serving the masses whole-heartedly.... Our Party members and those who have joined the revolutionary ranks are serving the people, regardless of whether or not they are aware of it, whether they occupy important leading positions or are merely privates, cooks or grooms. They are all of them directly or indirectly in the service of the people at different posts, and are therefore equal and honourable....

"Secondly, there is the standpoint of assuming full responsibility to the masses of the people......

"It is also necessary to understand the unity between responsibility to the people and responsibility to the leading bodies of our Party...the interests of the Party are identical with the interests of the people.... The interests of the people are the very interests of the party. The party has no particular interest of its own other than the people's interest.

"Thirdly, there is the standpoint of having faith in the people's self-emancipation...that the people alone are the real makers of history...that their own people alone are the real makers of history...that only through their own struggles and efforts can their emancipation be achieved, maintained and consolidated... merely through the efforts of the vanguard and without the people's genuine consciousness and mobilisation, emancipation of the people is impossible, history will not move forward and nothing can be accomplished...

".... Therefore, when the masses are not fully conscious, the duty of communists — the vanguard of the masses of the people— in carrying out any kind of work is to develop their consciousness by every effective and suitable means. This is the first step in our work which must be well done no matter how difficult it is or how much time it will take.

"Only when the first step has been taken, can we enter upon the second step. In other words, when the masses have reached the necessary level of consciousness, it is then our responsibility to guide them in their action — to guide them to organise and to fight. When this is brought about, we may further develop their conciousness through their actions. This is how we lead the masses step by step to fight for the basic slogans of the people as put forward by our Party ...[6]

"Fourthly, there is the standpoint of learning from the masses of the people.... We must have adequate knowledge and must be sufficiently experienced and vigilant before we can successfully raise the people's consciousness, lead their actions and serve them well. Learning is indispensable, if we are to acquire knowledge, experience and foresight.

"We may enrich our knowledge by studying Marxist-Leninist theories and by studying history and lessons of the people's struggles in foreign lands. We can also learn from our enemies. But what is most important is to learn from the masses of the people, since their knowledge and experience are the most abundant and most practical and their creative power is the greatest. This is why Comrade Mao Tse-tung has time and again told us to learn from the masses before we can educate them.... It will certainly be futile, if instead we should conceitedly devise a set of schemes out of our own imagination or mechanically introduce a set of

[6] Verbatim report on the Revision of the Party Constitution, delivered by Liu Shao Ch'i on May 14th, 1945, to the Seventh National Congress of the Chinese Communist Party. Foreign Languages Press—Peking, 1950—reproduced from *Revolution in a Chinese village Ten Mile Inn*' by Isabel and David Crook.

schemes from historical or foreign experiences in order to develop the consciousness of the masses and to guide them. In
order to learn unceasingly from the masses, we must not stand
isolated from the people for a single moment. If we do so our
knowledge will be greatly limited and certainly we cannot be
intelligent, informed, capable, or competent to give them leadership....

"In all sections of the masses there are generally to be found
relatively active elements, intermediate elements and backward
elements. In the initial stages the active elements are usually
in the minority, while the intermediate and the backward elements make up the broad masses. In accordance with the mass
line, attention must be paid to the majority, that is, the intermediate and the backward elements, otherwise the advanced sections will become isolated and nothing can be done satisfactorily.
The slogans of action and the form of struggle and of organisation
we put forward before the masses must be acceptable to the intermediate and the backward elements. The development of the
consciousness and the self-activity of the masses concerns chiefly
these people. A mass movement is possible only when these
people are awakened and inspired to action.

"We must pay particular attention to educating, uniting and
organising the active elements so that they may become the
nucleus of leadership among the masses. However, it must be
clearly understood that we are not organising the active elements merely for their own sake and that it is absolutely un-
permissible to isolate these elements from the intermediate and
backward masses. Our sole intention is to attract and set in
motion the intermediate and backward elements through the active
elements. In other words, it is for rallying the broadest possible
masses that the active elements are to be organised. If the
intermediate and backward elements are not yet awakened, we
must know how to enlighten them as well as how to wait for
them. If we are unwilling to wait, but recklessly rush forward
with a small number of the active elements following us, we
will isolate ourselves from the masses and end in failure.

"In our work, the rather low cultural level of the masses of
Chinese peasantry and other sections of the people, except for

the intelligentsia, make it all the more necessary to combine individual guidance with general directives and to set a whole campaign in motion by breaking through at one point. General directives will never succeed with masses of a low cultural level. This is due to the fact that the masses, especially the peasantry, usually consider problems on the basis of their personal experiences instead of on the basis of our general propaganda and slogans. In our work we should break through at one point to give an example to the masses and let them see and understand things for themselves. Only by giving examples to the masses can we encourage them, particularly the intermediate and backward elements, by affording them the opportunities and facilities to understand the problems thereby instilling in them confidence and courage to act under our Party's slogans and to culminate in an upsurge of mass enthusiasm."

From the above quotation it is clear that even in the Communist countries, they do not depend upon executive decrees or orders alone to bring about a change in the people, but prepare the people mentally and psychologically through an educational programme and propaganda for accepting the recommended improved practices or whatever government wants. If this is true of Communist countries, it should be more true of the countries like ours with democratic government and with equal if not lower cultural level of the masses than in China. The idea enunciated by Liu Shao Ch'i regarding active, intermediate and backward elements in the people also applies to our conditions and therefore, we have to plan our programmes in such a way that the majority is benefited with the active elements providing necessary leadership. Our programmes at present benefit mostly the 'Haves' and, therefore, if a real mass movement is to be launched, the programmes have to be such as would benefit the intermediate and backward masses who form the bulk of the population, if necessary, by replacing all out-moded and time-worn rules and regulations based on checks and rechecks, with proper and workable rules and regulations making governmental facilities and resources easily available to those who need them most.

In our case also, the leadership of the active elements would have to be gradually replaced through constructive programmes with the leadership of the intermediate and backward people. The programmes selected for the benefit of these people will also have to be such as may have wider application and appeal. The terms, conditions and facilities accompanying the programmes should be such as could be easily taken advantage of by the people in general and not by the privileged few as at present. Maybe the status of the people is so low that they are unable to take advantage of the programmes meant for their welfare on an individual basis. In such cases co-operatives and other joint enterprises will have to be given encouragement so that people at large are able to share the benefits which they are unable to obtain as individuals. All middlemen grabbing the income of the small producer will have to be eliminated. Loan and sub-sidy rules will have to be liberalised in favour of persons of smaller means. Steps will have to be taken to build confidence in the mass of people for raising their status by helping to build up some capital with them for investment and re-investment to increase their earnings on a progressive scale. The economic condition of the masses cannot be raised if there is distrust and fear of loss of its money on the part of government by thus help-ing them. The latter have to have a living faith in the bonafides of the masses in general and the masses in turn in government. It is only then, would the masses prosper and governments would be the real governments of the masses.

6. *Tremendous energies in the people*

People have tremendous unbelievable energies and capacities and they unfold themselves only when they are released by a spark of sincerity and will to action on the part of those who are responsible to initiate and arouse them. Democratic forces try to unfold these energies through a slow but lasting educational process while the Communist forces achieve the same through a sudden and quick educational process of brainwashing combined with force and fear. The effects produced in the latter case are temporary, lasting as long as the elements of force and fear are behind the change. Such a change may become permanent also if the elements of fear and force are continued for long so as to result in the change of habit and thinking.

The essence of working with the people lies in their education and changing their thinking and attitudes. If they are changed, a desire to gain knowledge and acquire skill to bring about the change comes as a natural corollary. This desire is like a young germinated seedling born from the seed sown in a favourable ground and, therefore, needs to be nurtured properly with adequate knowledge and skill to grow into an adult tree of mass upsurge.

7. *Initiating programmes amongst the people*

Should the extension worker initiate a programme by explaining it to a large gathering as a *Gram Sabha* meeting or through a few leaders who should carry the message to others? Experience shows that explaining a programme with a view to getting it adopted by the people, to a larger gathering as *Gram Sabha* meeting is not very helpful. This may be useful in some urgent political situations, but in taking up extension programmes, approach through a larger number does not often succeed. The programme takes roots better if it is explained to a few community leaders who become its protagonists. The extension worker has to find out such leaders and inspire and convince them about the programme he wants to initiate. These leaders should be encouraged to add to their numbers some followers each until gradually a larger number of people are imbued with a common interest and the programme is accepted by the people as their own.

Such a procedure for launching mass movements has been followed since times immemorial. There is hardly any religious and successful political movement which has not made a start with this kind of snowball process of gathering weight and momentum by having an inspired leader who gathered a few disciples around him and so inspired them with his enthusiasm and leadership and knit them together that they continued to carry on the movement even after he was no more. This was done by Buddha and repeated by Christ and Gandhi. Buddha had 5 such disciples, Christ 12 and Mahatma Gandhi a few more. Mahatma Gandhi's salt movement was started in the same way.

The extension workers in agricultural and community development programmes have also to spot out and build up leaders and help them to work with full initiative.

What is wrong with our programmes these days, is that we try to impose the programmes rather than build a spirit in the people. The community development programme requires building up the spirit first and then a project afterwards. Wherever the programmes in community development blocks are not making any headway, the reason always lies in the fact that the extension worker first tries to develop the programme and waits for the spirit to develop afterwards.

The All India Rural Credit Survey Committee appointed by the Reserve Bank of India in 1951 has also highlighted in the concluding remarks of its final report the importance of spiritual and emotional touch to all programmes of economic and human development. It observes as follows:

"There are two main facts about India: religion and poverty. It would be as foolish to ignore the one as the other. No endeavour that is great is likely to succeed in India unless the springs of action are derived from the living fount of religious feeling. No aim of the State in India can be so great as the abolition of poverty. In the pursuit of this aim, everything will fall short of success which gives only lip recognition to India's spiritual traditions and lip sympathy to India's poverty. There are signs today that not only the political consciousness, but the much deeper and more abiding spiritual awareness, of the country has been stirred to action by the distress and the inequality which have resided so long in thousands of its villages. Of extreme importance to India is the question whether all forces of enlightenment, spiritual, religious and social, no less than political, administrative and technical, will come together in a common pursuit, both informed and determined, of the economic good of the country.

"Any considered thesis concerning rural credit in India cannot help being in essence, though not in detailed exposition, a part of a much larger thesis concerning the economic good of India. This is inevitable because rural credit, seemingly both narrow and technical as a subject of enquiry, is in reality neither of these. In extent, it is as wide as rural society, which means practically as wide as the Indian nation. In content, it embraces all economic activities and purposes as they affect rural society, for credit is only a layer of such activities and has organic purpose only in so far as those activities have an organic purpose. Assuming this larger purpose to have the twofold aspect of achieving wealth and securing its equitable distribution, a programme of rural credit becomes inseparable, in its underlying concepts, not only from the end which is economic good, but from the means to be employed in the attainment of the end. Those means, to be significant for India, have to conform to the values of the Indian tradition. One feature of that tradition may be recalled. At widely different times and in widely different parts of the country there have arisen religious leaders in India whose aim was spiritual good and whose endeavour it was to place within the reach of all the means of achieving such good. Each such effort was non-violently conceived and non-violently conducted; it had the appeal and motive force of a mission and, not infrequently, its organisation bore signs of careful forethought and attention. Essentially the same means, employed in the pursuit of economic good, have perhaps this difference, that they hold greater promise of attaining the object postulated. For one thing, there is nothing yet in human history to disprove — just as there is nothing in it yet to demonstrate — that economic welfare in its highest sense cannot be achieved, even where it is most lacking, by the planned, deliberate and organised effort of a government, relentless as to purpose but not ruthless as to means, provided the effort is not only emotionally impelled but is scientifically guided. In this latter aspect, a whole apparatus of technique, knowledge and research, comparatively recent and painstakingly accumulated, is available to governments, if only they will make use of it, through the development of the social sciences of economics and sociology and of the science no less than art of public administration. It is irrelevant whether economic good is or is not a lesser objective than spiritual good. The fact remains that economic good is the highest practicable objective so far as governments are concerned. In India, the process of increasing and more equitably distributing the economic good must, on purely rational grounds, be conceived in terms of rural India. The larger thesis, in which our concrete recommendations can find place only as part, is that what India most needs today is a comprehensive and determined programme of rural regeneration which has the ethical impulse and emotional momentum of its highest traditions; which has, moreover, the calculated design of project that is scientifically conceived and scientifically organised; and which above all, attempts to render to rural India, in the economic realm, those opportunities for growth and fulfilment which, without distinction between man and man, but with especial compassion for the weak and the disadvantaged, more than one religious leader at more than one period of the country's history attempted to render to the masses of India in the realm of the spirit."

Says Sampurnanand in his book on Indian Socialism, "the focal point of all planning and organisation is the individual. Society and all its organs are for the individual and not he for them. The aim of the reformer and the revolutionary will not be merely a dialectical study of the environment to helping forces tending to acquire preponderance as a historical necessity but to study innate nature of man and the tendencies that result from it and help to create an environment that will be most conducive to their satisfaction".

Nehru as quoted by Sampurnanand felt the same way: "It is often said that there is a sense of frustration and depression in India and the old buoyancy of spirit is not to be found at a time when enthusiasm and hard work are most needed. It is due to our not having a philosophy of life, and indeed the world also is suffering from this lack of philosophical approach. In our efforts to ensure natural prosperity of the country, we have not paid any attention to the spiritual element in human nature. Therefore, in order to give the individual and the nation a sense of purpose, something to live for and if necessary to die for, we have to revive some philosophy of life and give, in the wider sense of the word, a spiritual background to our thinking."

In the ultimate analysis, it is the quality of man that matters and so let us all dedicate in whatever position we are, to improve the quality of man, first of all in our own self and then afterwards in others. Let education of the man give him a sense of purpose, something to live for and if necessary to die for, be started first. As soon as the desire of giving a sense of purpose to life is kindled in him, it should then be enlarged to the size of the flame till a fire for emancipation from the old rut and achieving the objective spreads all round.

This can be achieved only through a constant programme of education whose main aim has to be man-making. "Education," said Swami Vivekananda, "as late as in the nineteenth century, is not the amount of information that is put into your brain and runs riot there, undigested, all your life. We must have life-building, man-making, character-making, assimilation of ideas. If you have assimilated five ideas and made them your life and character, you have more education than any man who has got by heart a whole library. If education is identical with information, the libraries are the greatest sages in the world, and encyclopaedias are the *rishis*".

Education in our case has to be more through practice, examples, demonstrations, study tours, group discussions, meetings and practical training than through books. Its main aim has to be men-making. The main responsibility for this education has to be shouldered in the beginning by the official machinery which in itself has to have a prior training. It has also to spot out simultaneously the wise, the learned, the selfless and dedicated workers from among the people themselves. They then, have to be motivated, trained, constantly guided and encouraged to shoulder the future responsibility of changing the historically conditioned old attitudes, abilities, propensities and behaviour of men and social systems of the people, which have not been conducive to dissemination of modern knowledge, to development of an enterprising spirit in the common man and to make the best use of the available resources. This has to be an everlasting process and this is what the Community Development Programme has to constantly strive for.

The process of education of the people would not be complete if it is left to only creating a desire, awareness or determination in the people or giving a know-how to improve their lot. It has to be followed with provision of additional resources and proper environment conducive to translation of what is learnt, in a way

that the common man is able to avail and take advantage of
them without procedural or constitutional delays. The present
thinking in the country is in the right direction, but there is still
more talk, preaching, urging, and exhortation than action, more
inconsistencies than consistencies, more formalities in working
than informalities and more procedural tangles than facilities to
work which give progress only a slow climb without appreciable
visible change in the method of production, social structure, values,
and economic condition of the people.

CHAPTER II

THE PROGRAMMES

ADOPTION OF programmes or improved techniques by the people leads in course of time to permanent socio-economic and psychological changes affecting their lives. It also changes their thinking and values in life. The changes are permanent, if:

1. The benefits accruing from the programmes have been tasted and taken advantage of by the adopters.
2. The continued adoption of the programmes is well within the resources of the adopters.
3. The local conditions under which the programmes are adopted do not change materially so as to make their continued adoption difficult.
4. Adopted programmes are properly continued or maintained and do not go out of use.

If the improved techniques are productive, they lead to increased income. Increased income in turn results in increased expenditure. The items on which the expenditure is generally made differ from man to man and area to area according to social customs, habits, traditions and economic conditions and taboos. Keeping all these in view, the items of expenditure can be arranged more or less in the following priority:

1. Better clothing;
2. Entertainment and socio-religious ceremonies;
3. Sending children to schools;
4. Better housing facilities;

53

5. Buying ornaments;
6. Increased litigation;
7. Tendency to aspire for leadership and spending on it;
8. Better sanitation;
9. Better medical facilities;
10. Better food; and
11. Re-investment in production.

This priority cannot be said to be rigid. It changes according to circumstances and factors given above. Illiterate or semi-literate persons of inadequate or moderate means generally like to spend their income first on wear, secondly on entertainment and then on other items. Middle-class persons first prefer to spend it on luxury items, education of children, ornaments, and a little bit on better food. Persons of better means, however, prefer to spend it mostly on education of their children, luxury items and construction of a house.

Whatever may be the priority of expenditure amongst persons of different status it is certain that additional production and better nutrition gets almost the lowest priority. This is also one of the reasons why improved techniques are not being adopted and even if they are adopted, they are adopted in most cases temporarily.

This trend places a heavy responsibility on the extension worker. He has not only to popularise the improved techniques amongst the people, but also to give a forceful direction to investing the major part of the increased income resulting from the adoption of improved techniques, in the business for a few years followed by better nutrition, education of the children, better clothes and then on other welfare items. Only when such a priority in expenditure is adhered to, there can be any national saving, re-investment of this saving in the business and increase in national income and standard of living of the people.

(1) Programmes for adoption

Depending upon how different programmes affect the people, they can be classified according to:

(*a*) The number of people affected or benefited. (*b*) The resources required, (c) The need of the people, (d) The time factor involved in execution, (e) The benefits received, and (f) The sequence of execution.

(a) *The number of people affected or benefited*

The programmes according to the number of people affected or benefited by them can be categorised into:

(i) Those needed by groups of villages, blocks, districts, and States, as roads, major irrigation works, *etc.*

(ii) Those needed by the community as a whole as schools, roads, improved agricultural implements, culverts, pavement of lanes, *etc.*

(iii) Those needed by a small section or a group within the community *e.g.* wells, hand pumps, culverts, cattle sheds, pavement of lanes, minor irrigation works, *etc.*, and

(iv) Those needed by individuals as cattle sheds, minor irrigation works, improved agricultural practices, *pucca* compost pits.

Each block/area has to divide the programmes into the above categories and take action in respect of each of them separately.

For programmes of the (i) category, the representatives of the people or Governments of different areas or States are brought together to think jointly on the problem, plan and its execution. These representatives in turn persuade and enthuse the concerned people or Governments and initiate them into action.

For programmes of the (ii) category, the entire community is enthused and mobilised directly or generally through its leaders. The degree of participation of the community in such programmes depends upon the interest created by the extension worker in the people.

For programmes of the (iii) and (iv) categories, beneficiaries have to be approached individually or in groups and initiated into action.

(b) *The resources required*

According to the resources required for execution, the programmes can be classified into 3 categories as below:

(i) Those to be undertaken entirely with the local resources,

(ii) Those to be undertaken partly with the help of local resources and partly with governmental or any other outside aid, and

(iii) Those to be undertaken entirely with the help of governmental or any other aid.

Programmes under (i) depend upon the local initiative generated by a motivation and helped by technical guidance and supervision by an outside agency. The execution is carried out by the individuals or the community concerned.

Programmes under (ii) depend upon the local initiative as well as the initiative of the outside agency and are combined with some promise of aid—financial or technical. The execution of such programmes is carried out by the individual or the community concerned.

Programmes under (iii) depend entirely on the initiative of the outside agency as that of a government. Local people may also be associated with them, but the entire execution is generally done by the sponsoring agency.

As the individuals, groups or the entire community are not very much a party to the execution of programmes falling under the category (iii), the discussion below has been kept restricted mainly to the programmes of categories (i) and (ii) with which the people are directly concerned. In the discussion, the programmes falling in category (ii) have been designated as aided programmes and those falling in category (i) as unaided programmes. Aid here means generally the financial aid.

The programmes undertaken by the people without any aid by harnessing their own resources, talent and energies are generally known to spread faster than the programmes that are dependent wholly or partly on outside aid. Being executed and completed with the people's own determination and will, they generate a feeling of self-reliance and confidence in them to plan effectively, manage their own affairs and assume greater and greater responsibilities for their future welfare. As the execution of such programmes progresses and the people get a glimpse of the vast latent potentialities, a vista of happiness providing necessary confidence and self-reliance is unfolded before them. This gives them strength and confidence which if sustained takes them forward on the road to happiness.

In the aided programmes, the aid is either given at the start or after a part of the entire work has been completed. The people realise the benefit and feel grateful for the aid if it is given at the start, but if it is given after the work is completed, it does not really serve any purpose. It fails to keep up the enthusiasm with which the people started. Aid gives the best dividends if it is given at the proper moment. The rules and procedures regulating the grant of aid are usually so cumbersome that the beneficiary is seldom able to derive full benefits from it. Often he has to spend considerable money for proper or questionable purpose before he is able to get the aid.

Aid is generally given for new programmes with a view to popularising them among the people. It is gradually discontinued when the programmes become popular and the people's inertia is broken.

Most of the aided programmes start with good success initially. Their pace, however, usually slows down as the aid is gradually reduced or stopped, or when those eligible for it have availed of it leaving only those who are not eligible for it. Aid if examined closely is generally availed of under our conditions only by the 'Haves' and not by 'Have-nots'. The real benefit from the aid can be derived only when it is given on a sliding scale with the 'Have-nots' getting a greater share than the 'Haves'.

As pointed out above, aided programmes seem to move faster initially, but after some time the very aid itself becomes a bottleneck and a hindrance to the rapid extension of such programmes. As soon as it is withdrawn the people do not adopt them in the hope of getting it again. Aid when improperly given acts as a deterrent to the further extension of the programme, because instead of generating a spirit of self-reliance it creates an expectation for undeserved assistance and a spirit of dependence.

Several wrong tendencies are seen to develop in almost all the aided programmes. One such tendency is inflation of the estimates for getting a greater share of the aid by deceitful means. This is one of the reasons why the aided programmes do not in the majority of cases generate a real community feeling or desire among the people to work for themselves. Not only the beneficiaries but the workers also in a few cases become a party to such inflation of estimates. This is because more than what they can achieve is expected of them within a short time. They are not given enough time for educating and enthusing the people to think themselves about their programmes. Before they are able to do so, pressure is brought to bear on them to get the pace of expenditure expedited. The moment they feel the pressure they try to get the programmes executed by becoming a party to inflation of estimates and ignoring real facts. This is done with the help of a few opportunist leaders despite the fact that favourable atmosphere for adoption of the programme in question is not created in the village.

Some workers have also been seen to become a party to inflation of estimates because they want to oblige a particular person or a leader to whom he had been under obligation in the past.

Whenever aided programmes are started with an imperative time-limit for their completion, they lead to the demoralisation of workers. There should be no inflexible time schedule attached to the aided programmes, because such programmes to be effective and self-propelling require considerable prior working with the people for initiating and arousing them to action. Usually a certain minimum period of time should be allowed to a worker to educate the people and initiate them into action before expecting any results or expenditure.

It would also not be always correct to say that aided programmes do not generate any self-reliance and determination among the people. Much depends upon how the aid is given. If the aid is given with a view to utilising and spending funds or to obliging individuals or groups or the community without stimulating their thought and action, it is not received in proper spirit and correctly utilised. If, on the other hand, the aid is given when the individuals or the people have been properly initiated it helps to create in them a spirit of self-reliance and a desire to work harder. If the aid is given without keeping this object in view, it is almost wasted even though it may result in some physical achievement. Examples of starting innumerable community orchards and afforestation blocks in Community Development areas can be cited to prove this contention. Most of them today have no plants or fencing to justify the aid given to them. This tragedy was due to the fact that such orchards and afforestation blocks were laid out without prompting the people to think and execute the programme themselves, but only to spend funds and to create show pieces by making the village *Pradhans* or *Panchayats* and its funds as the instrument and symbol of people's participation. The *Pradhans* or other village leaders also felt interested and elated because a good number of high officers and personalities visited their villages in connection with the opening ceremonies or showing round these show pieces to important visitors.

Shramdan Programmes

Of the resources of the people, *Shramdan* is one of the most potent resources available with them. This resource is a boon for areas/countries which have plenty of man-power.

Considerable enthusiasm was created in early days of Community Development programmes for *Shramdan*. People came forward to offer it willingly, but when they found their *Shramdan* being wasted or washed down into the drains and the rivers due to erosion by wind and rains, they became cold. A calculated and well planned *Shramdan* is a form of capital formation and a natural asset. Capital is generally produced from additional capital, but China is setting an example in trying to produce capital by harnessing and converting its vast human resources into capital consisting of large national projects. They are able to do it by annexing all surplus agricultural production from collective farms and by utilising this surplus for feeding the surplus agricultural population and making them work on construction works of national interest. India with its inadequate capital

resources can also follow this example with modification to suit
its genius. We also possess the asset of man-power which China
has. We can be said to have been following this example but
much of our efforts are wasted due to idealism and bad planning.
Test works organised as relief measures or *Shramdan* organised
from time to time if properly planned, can all be utilised for
capital formation. What is necessary is proper planning, direction, technical advice and schemes for maintenance of what has
already been achieved. Items for test works and *Shramdan* in the
beginning have to be as far as possible such which help to increase agricultural production and income of the people directly
or indirectly.

(c) *The need of the people*

The programme on the basis of needs can be classified into:

(i) *Programmes for which need is apparent, felt or pronounced*:   These needs are known to the people and they desire
their solution without any waiting. Examples of such needs in
the villages are: digging of a drainage channel usually passing
through various villages, construction of a road, establishment
of a hospital, provision of new irrigation works or channels on
tubewells, control of stray and wild animals, and construction of
a bridge for making the area accessible throughout the year.

(ii) *Programmes for which the need is latent or has to be
created and made pronounced*: These needs are also very vital.
They are slowly and slowly brought to the surface and made
pronounced till people accept them as their vital needs, through
education and by convincing and motivating them. All new techniques or programmes come under this category. They are selected
by the extension agency for adoption by the people on the basis
of survey, requirement and resources of the people, and recommendation by the extension worker or his seniors. Examples of
such needs are: increase in agricultural production, construction
of masonry compost pits, provision of good drinking water, provision of medical facilities, construction of sanitary latrines, construction of sanitary hearths (*choolhas*), and construction of good
Kharanjas (paved lanes).

A question is often asked by the extension workers whether

they should approach the people direct with a programme which the extension worker selects himself on the basis of his own experience or on the basis of experience or orders of the senior officers or should they find out the felt-needs of the people, help them to fulfil those needs and then guide them to plan and execute other programmes of benefit to them. This is quite a controversial subject; for experience shows that an extension worker can proceed either way and achieve success. Presenting a new programme straightway before the people often proves more useful than by making an approach first through their felt-need. What people could do easily with their resources themselves, they already do, but whatever they are not able to do with their own resources themselves, that generally becomes their felt-need.

Most of the felt-needs are such as require a large amount of funds, which an extension worker cannot commit at the start. A few of such felt-needs may require even joint planning and working by several villages. Too much emphasis on approaching the people through their felt-needs may thus not be a practical method. If it is however, possible to satisfy the felt-needs by pooling the local and the available official resources, they should be satisfied first; for such a satisfaction leads to a lot of encouragement and building of faith in the people for their betterment.

Working on the basis of felt-needs, the extension worker should try to find out the felt-needs from the people themselves. When they start telling about them, they must be asked questions like: How can this felt-need be solved? How many people would be benefited? How much work they can do? What outside help they want?

Care is, however necessary to ensure that no suggestion is made by the extension worker in the beginning: for all suggestions should come from them. Experience has shown that if questioning is done in this direction and the extension worker takes the people slowly and slowly through their own arguments and analysis to plan a solution for their felt-needs, the response is better than if the extension worker suggests a plan himself.

The workers in finding out the felt-needs and in helping the people to satisfy them, generally make a mistake by announcing in advance the government help that could be made available to them. Such an approach from the very beginning gives the people an impression that perhaps government may undertake the project itself. If such hopes are raised, they create difficulties. The real community spirit works only when the community tries to shoulder responsibility for all that is within its means to do and only expects government to do what it cannot do. The extension workers who do not work on this principle, seldom succeed in generating a real community spirit in the people.

The direct programme of the unpronounced-need-approach is generally much simpler and cheaper than the apparent or felt-need approach. The extension worker in the latent felt-need approach selects some programme suiting to the area and the people and which gives the quickest returns or success, arranges their demonstrations, convinces the people and then persuades them for their adoption. When a few such programmes are adopted by the people and their income increases, they develop a faith in the extension worker and listen to his advice. Fulfilment of the felt-needs of the people can then more easily be taken up with the help of people themselves. They would be ready to do what they could, having experienced the benefit out of the new method suggested to them. Several examples of starting with direct programmes and helping to solve felt-needs after receiving success in them, are noticeable in Etawah Pilot Project (Uttar Pradesh) and at several other places.

(d) The time factor involved in execution

According to the time factor involved in execution, the programmes can be classified as:

(*i*) Short period programmes requiring from a fraction of an hour to about a year. They give quick and immediate results and are very good for convincing the people in a short time and initiating them to take up further responsibilities. The examples of such programmes are use of new implements and techniques, use of fertilisers, use of insecticides, *etc.*

(*ii*) Long period programmes requiring more than a year. Their execution is spread over a long period and they take considerable time to show tangible results and are more expensive to launch than short period programmes. The examples of such programmes are improvement in the cattle of the area through artificial insemination and other cattle breeding programmes, construction of roads, bridges, drainage channels, tubewells, *etc.*

On account of slow results and heavy expenditure, they are often given the last priority by the worker who concentrates on programmes which yield quick results. Often long-term programmes are never taken up even though they may be basically important for making the foundation of development work strong.

Improvement of cattle is an important long-term programme for it provides almost the entire draught power for agriculture in the country besides providing milk and other commodities. Such programmes take about 10 years to show tangible results. If such programmes are given low priority, the foundation for sound agricultural development continues to remain weak.

Urgency demands that no programmes, whether short-term or long-term should be neglected. A compromise has, therefore, to be found out so that both may go simultaneously. A start should normally be made with important long-term programmes and along with them a few short-term programmes may also be taken up to show quick results.

Another example of long-term programmes is the construction of bridges, and roads in inaccessible areas as of district Hamirpur in Uttar Pradesh. This district is bounded by two rivers and thus loses all road contact with the rest of the State for quite a long time of the year. It is a surplus area from the agricultural stand point, but as communications are very poor, agricultural produce is sold at very cheap rates. Sometimes the difference in price between other important cities of the State and Hamirpur is of the order of Rs. 15 to 21 per quintal. If in an area like this, bridges are constructed on the rivers surrounding the district, it will have opened up the district for better economic development. What perhaps extension workers could not achieve for several years, could have been easily achieved by the construction of bridges. Construction of bridges in such areas leads to sudden rise in the income of the people on account of better facilities for transport. Immediate impact on the income in turn leads people to think for better means of production and living.

In a programme of agricultural development such important factors are rarely taken into account by those who are responsible for agricultural development. It is seldom realised that programmes like construction of bridges and roads can also step up agricultural production and the income of the people. It is true that such bridges do not directly come within the purview of their department, but they do come in the overall planning of the State for agricultural development. The same applies to rural electrification programmes.

(e) Benefits received

According to the benefits received, the programmes can be classified into:

(*i*) Economic or production programmes — Their adoption leads to increased production and income of the people. Examples of such programmes are application of fertilizers, cultivation of new crops, introduction of improved implements and machines, use of green manures, legumes, *etc.*

(*ii*) Welfare programmes — Their adoption leads to better living and thinking. Examples of such programmes are construction of wells for drinking water, sanitary latrines, culverts, small bridges, roads, hospitals, installation of pipes for drinking water, pavement of village lanes, *etc.*

The question is often asked as to which of these programmes should be started first. Some people believe that production programmes should be taken up first and they should be closely followed up by welfare programmes. Others think that the welfare programmes should be taken up simultaneously and even before, for they believe that if people get glimpses of better living, they will like to adopt improved methods of production and increase their income. Both the ways of thinking can be correct in certain circumstances, but seeing the economic condition of the country, it seems more appropriate to agree with the first view, for unless production and income of the people were increased, they would not be able to adopt any welfare programme and even if they adopted them, it will be at the cost of utilising the income received from increased production which in the normal course should be re-invested for more production and income. The average annual per capita income of the people in India is about Rs. 291.6' or a little over Rs. 24.00 per month. This income is not considered sufficient even for bare subsistence not to speak of amenities and luxuries. Food should always come first and other things afterwards. It, therefore, becomes imperative that when food is scarce or in short supply, all programmes relating to food production should get top priority. It is only when agricultural production increases substantially and farmers have enough marketable surplus, other programmes should be stressed. Even for a few years till enough surpluses are available, a considerable portion of the income from increased agricultural production should be ploughed back every year to intensify the agricultural programme. This is necessary in the interest of agricultural production in the country as well as in the interest of the farmers for increasing their income and thereby their standards of living.

Industrialisation should always go hand in hand with agricultural production. Even in industrial programmes, industries which help to increase agricultural production or supplement agriculture should be given priority, along with other vital industries. This step is necessary because both the programmes are complementary to each other. Agricultural production cannot increase unless improved agricultural implements, fertilizers, electricity to run tube-wells and other irrigation works, pesticides, plant protection equipment, *etc.* are not produced through industrialisation. Wide use of improved agricultural practices, therefore, presupposes industrialisation as an accomplished fact. Industrialisation on the other hand, cannot be accomplished unless there is surplus agricultural production to be used as raw material, to feed the industrial population and to provide additional purchasing power to the 70 per cent rural population for consuming the goods produced. Increased purchasing power can come only when there is surplus agricultural production to feed the city population, to keep a buffer stock for the rainy day, and to provide raw materials to the industry.

' This figure is for 1959-60 and is based on 1948-49 prices.

4

Welfare programmes should always come next to agricultural and industrial programmes when the country and the individuals are able to build up enough saving after ploughing back a major part of it to intensification of production. Those welfare programmes which however, help the growth of both the agricultural and industrial programmes should be taken up simultaneously.

The Community Development Programme in India was started as a multipurpose programme. It was mistaken to be a programme of all-round development of the people in the beginning because it was apprehended that if it was not taken to be as such, it would result in imbalance and lop-sided development of the people. This was not a healthy view as Community Development Programme in India had to cater in any case to the needs of 70 per cent of its people engaged in agriculture. Agriculture in itself is a multi-faced programme. It entails within its purview all programmes which help to increase agricultural production and income of the rural people—right from production, marketing, storage, consumption and distribution of agricultural produce to construction of irrigation works, soil conservation and reclamation methods, drainage works, processing of agricultural produce including fruit and vegetable preservation, milk, wool, meat and fish production, control of floods, organisation of co-operatives, youth clubs, and training of village leaders, farmers, members of village *Panchayats* and co-operatives, *etc*. It includes even construction of roads, control of malaria and cattle diseases, establishment of agro-industries as manufacture of agricultural implements, pesticides, bullock carts, and tubes and tyres, development of power stations to energise tubewells and agro-industries, arrangements for the sale of goods like cycle, small machines, *etc*. When agriculture, therefore, has so many facets, there should have been no apprehension of lop-sided development of the people.

Numerous instances can be quoted to show that whenever and wherever agricultural production increased, the people themselves with little education and guidance undertook their own welfare programmes with considerably lesser cost to government than otherwise. Whenever welfare programmes are taken first or side by side with the agricultural programmes, they hamper agricultural development with the result that neither progresses satisfactorily. Agricultural development suffers for want of sufficient attention and welfare programmes for want of people's share of money to match with the government aid.

(f)   The sequence of execution

According to the sequence of execution the programmes can be divided into: (i)   Main programmes, and (ii) Subsidiary programmes.

The main programmes are taken up first and followed by subsidiary or feeder programmes. A common mistake is to start the main programme and not to follow it with feeder programmes. The result is that the main programmes succeed for a short time after which they fail to expand on account of several limiting factors resulting from the lack of follow up by feeder programmes. Two case histories in this connection would explain the matter better.

(a) The popularisation of Japanese method of paddy cultivation is one of the many improved practices recommended by the agriculture departments in India. The programme was started in the country in 1953-54. Its progress over the years has been as below:

Year	Area in acres[s]
1953-54	0.401 millions
1954-55	1.319 ,,
1955-56	2.096 ,,
1956-57	2.373 ,,
1957-58	3.997 ,,
1958-59	5.662 ,,
1959-60	7.179 ,,

[s] Figures based on letter No. F. 1-1/63C and FE dated Jan. 4, 1964, from Dy. Director Co-ordination, Government of India, Ministry of Food and Agriculture (Department of Agriculture) New Delhi.

The above figures show that starting with an achievement of 0.401 million acres under the Japanese method of paddy cultivation in 1953-54, the figures rose to 8.287 million acres in 1960-61, *i.e.* after a period of eight years. The achievement of 8.287 million acres was against the total paddy area of 83.335 million acres in the entire country in 1960-61. It came to only 9.94 per cent of the total paddy area, which is insignificant considering the benefit of higher yields varying from 15 to 50 per cent resulting from the adoption of the method in various parts of the country. If adoption of the method gives profitable returns to the farmers, why then the adoption has been slow being only 9.94 per cent after a period of eight years. Conservatism of the farmers is occasionally pointed out as the reason for slow adoption. Whether this is true or not, one thing is certain that the programme suffers from several limitations on account of which its pace of adoption is slow. The author has studied this problem very closely. On the basis of this study the following factors have been found to limit its expansion:

(*i*) In the beginning, transplantation in lines with the help of ropes, requires two additional hands than in the local method. It adds to the cost of transplanting. The farmers, therefore, do not like to incur all this extra expenditure. In many areas, women do the entire transplanting and the farmer carts the seedlings from the nursery. In such areas the farmers do not find it possible on account of scarcity of labour at the time of transplanting to employ two additional hands.

(*ii*) Difficulty in getting fertilizers in small quantities.

(*iii*) Inter-culture with the help of Japanese paddy weeder or some other implement is not carried out on account of the fact that majority of the extension workers do not themselves possess experience of working the improved implements especially the Japanese paddy weeder.

Had the workers ensured removal of these limitations by starting the following feeder programmes, the progress would have been much faster:

(*i*) Proper training of the workers and the farmers in running the Japanese paddy weeders.

(*ii*) Training of women and other labourers in transplanting in lines.

(*iii*) Popularisation of devices for transplanting in lines other than through the use of ropes which required two additional labourers such as use of bamboos, triangular transplanters and practice in transplanting without ropes.

(*iv*) Persuading gang-labour leaders directly or through *Gaon Sabhas* to take contracts for transplanting in lines, and inter-culture, and farmers to pay slightly higher wages than before.

(*v*) Opening a large number of sales points for distribution of fertilizers and making credit for their purchase readily available.

(*b*) A certain State in the country decided to popularise the cultivation of Soyabean — a crop rich in protein. It distributed large quantities of seeds. The cultivators grew these seeds and sold the produce to the agriculture department. This went on for two or three years till it was beyond the means of government to purchase the entire produce. It then left purchasing the seeds. There was no regular market for the produce in the State as people never used it before. The result was that the grain produced did not find any ready market. The only purchaser was government and it did not then purchase. The result was obvious. The cultivators gave up its cultivation.

Had this programme also been followed up with the feeder programme of popularising the use of Soyabean as food and feed, a demand for its use would have been created. All government farms should also have learnt to utilise it as cattle feed. In the absence of these follow up programmes, the main programme also fizzled out after an initial success. All money and energies thus spent over the introduction of Soyabean were wasted.

(2) *Speed in programme*

There are three stages in extention of all programmes :

(*a*) Initiation,

(*b*) Expansion, and

(*c*) Saturation.

Each of these stages requires some time depending on the organising ability of the workers, response of the people and arrangement of timely supplies. If all these conditions are favourable, the three stages are travelled with the fastest speed.

Initiation is the demonstration stage. It helps people to know about the programme and to build up their attitudes for its adoption through educating and imparting them the required knowledge and skill about the programme. This is a very important stage as almost the entire success in acceptance of the programme depends upon its successful execution.

Good initiation creates momentum of its own which coupled with good organisation of supplies and services required for the expanding programme, greatly helps to achieve the expansion and saturation stage.

If initiation is defective, there is hardly any momentum and as the result the other two stages are seldom reached. There appears to be a little advance towards expansion stage under this condition due to a constant official pressure but this advance is not commensurate with the labour put in. It comes to a stop after some time. There is also sometimes reversion to the original state if the official pressure is withdrawn.

If initiation is proper, expansion of the programme takes place in geometrical progression, for it then becomes people's own programme who come to believe in its utility or efficacy.

Of the three stages, that of initiation is the most delicate and difficult one. It requires greater time than the other two stages. One should not expect any adoption of the programme during the stage of initiation. One of the commonest defects in the present day official machinery is to expect adoption of the programme from the day the order is issued. No time is given to the workers to stimulate thinking and educate the people in the details and utility of the programme. The result is that when the programme is started, there appears to be a great enthusiasm in the workers about it, but when it is not adopted by the people with the speed expected of the workers, they feel lost and very much dejected. The programme may be good for the people, but unless people have been properly educated, initiated and prepared for its adoption it would not be liked and adopted by them, although individuals here and there may adopt it at the instance of official workers or due to automatic expansion. When this situation arises, either the programme is criticised or the people are blamed. It is forgotten that basically extension work is a process of education.

Often unnecessary haste in launching and executing programmes in the beginning results in the loss of energy and enthusiasm of the workers in the course of time. This is because of resistance from the people who are not properly initiated, educated and enthused to move with the same speed as the workers, and of several shortcomings and mistakes which are generally committed when planning is done in a hurry. Often greater speed in execution of the programmes in the beginning results in its slowing down or completely withering away after sometime. The better course is always to make a modest beginning and then expand the programme slowly and slowly as people become convinced about the benefits accruing from it. Several poultry projects in the Community Development areas have failed because the workers out of sheer enthusiasm tried to establish bigger units of poultry with 100 birds or so without taking into account the heavy responsibility they entailed and the fact whether or not the breeders were mentally prepared or properly educated to look after such units. The result was that most of such units failed and are no more there because the breeders who were advised to keep such units could no longer manage them properly. In many cases, the entire stock died for want of proper veterinary aid. If the extension worker had tried to establish smaller units of 10 birds or so, the breeders would have been able to manage them properly and even if they failed, they would not have lost much. As breeders gathered experience, the size of their units should have been increased with the help of their own produced stock of eggs and birds.

(3) *Goal in extension programmes*

Goal can be defined as the potential or the maximum limit to which a programme can be developed. Goal is different from target, but it is synonymous when it is equal to the target. A goal is necessary to be fixed for all programmes before they are started in a certain area. For example, if the programme is Japanese method of paddy cultivation, then it has to be found out as to what is the area under paddy which can be brought under Japanese method of paddy cultivation. This area would be the goal for bringing under this improved practice. Similarly, in the case of artificial insemination programme, it has to be estimated as to how many females are required to be pregnated. Based on these figures how many artificial insemination centres and subcentres and how many breeding bulls for natural service and artificial insemination centres will be required to cover the entire population of cattle. This will be the goal to achieve. A reasonable time-limit has to be fixed for achieving the goal. After it has been fixed it is divided into targets for achieving in a certain period. Target is, therefore, part of the goal to be achieved in a fixed time-limit.

Quite often the targets are fixed without finding out the ultimate goals in extension. Knowledge about goals gives an idea of the magnitude of the problem. In the absence of any clear idea about the magnitude of the problem, the workers think mainly in narrow terms of fulfilling the target and not in wider perspective of achieving or creating necessary conditions for reaching the ultimate goal. The small achievements that are secured do not in many cases make any appreciable impact on the problem. If the goal is clear, the extension worker shall always be thinking as to how and how soon to achieve the goal. Depending upon the capability, organising skill and understanding of the problem, some workers would reach the goal in comparatively lesser time than others.

One of the reasons why several extension programmes do not seem to make any appreciable impact on the people is that they are initiated by fixing small targets and are continued as such. The exact magnitude of the problem sufficient to make an impact on the people is not imagined. Can it be imagined that distribution of 100 to 200 thousand chicks, training of one to two thousands of poultry breeders or opening of a few government poultry or duck centres in a span of five years in States like Uttar Pradesh, Maharashtra or Rajasthan, Madhya Pradesh with populations ranging from 40 millions to 73 millions would create any appreciable impact on the programme of poultry or egg production sufficient for consumption of such large populations. In such a case, the programme may seem to be making some progress in inspections or progress reports, but in actual practice it does not make any appreciable dent in the problem. Beginning shall always be from a dot leading to a man-hole. When large areas or populations are concerned, the execution of the programme has to be so planned that it covers as large a population, in as short a time with as little resources as possible. Based on this thinking, it has to be reconsidered whether planning for various programmes, especially important agricultural and animal husbandry programmes, has been properly thought out or not. It has to be considered whether or not ultimate goals have been kept in view while planning. If they have been kept in view, have suitable programmes been accordingly thought of to give the benefits of these programmes to the majority of the people in the minimum possible time. If the goals fixed for the various items in our plans are analysed and connected with the sanctioned or proposed schemes, it would be found that a good number of them are not comprehensive enough to produce the desired result or impact on the people. No wonder that the results in such cases are obvious and we do not go far from where we started.

Resources may be a limiting factor in extending a particular programme. When areas and populations to be covered are large, the expenditure of governmental resources should be planned in a way that it creates those resources which people cannot easily create by their existing resources. It has also to be so planned that large areas or persons could avail and take advantage of the resources resulting from the expenditure.

(4) *Important problems affecting programmes*

Local problems have a great bearing on the acceptance of programmes by the people. Of these, there are some which are peculiar to a particular area, while there are others which are generally encountered everywhere. A few examples of local problems, and how they influence the execution of other programmes are given below:

(a) Problem of stray cattle

The animal population in India, according to the 1956 livestock census, has been estimated to be about 300 millions. This is about 25 per cent less than the human population. An average animal requires much more food than a human being. When there is already a shortage of food for human beings in the country, how can such a large population of cattle be fed? It is estimated that about 70 per cent of the agricultural production of the country is consumed by the animals in the shape of feeds and fodders and only about 30 per cent remains for human consumption. Most of the Western countries which have tried to increase their agricultural production have succeeded:

(i) by replacing cattle power with machine power thereby saving the food which is consumed by cattle and reducing the cost of cultivation, and

(ii) by encouraging people to keep fewer animals of better quality than large number of animals of inferior quality and thus saving precious feed and fodder.

As against these two important methods of increasing agricultural production, the tendency with the majority of the people here is to own a larger number of cattle heads than they can actually feed even though they may be of poor quality. They keep them for milk, butter, meat and manure production and power for agriculture even though they do not have adequate land for grazing, or fodder and grain production. They are, therefore, obliged to let them loose to graze the crops of the other farmers. The problem of stray cattle damaging crops of the farmers has of late become very serious. It has been aggravated by large scale preventive measures against diseases which have been taken by the State animal husbandry departments in the country and due to legislation banning cow slaughter in several states.

The problem of stray cattle, where it exists, has resulted in the following situations:

(*i*) Farmers do not like to sow any crops in off seasons for example in the summer months. They are afraid lest their crops may be grazed by the stray cattle. The programme of popularising summer crops in such areas does not succeed.

(*ii*) Farmers have to spend considerable energy in protecting their crops and saving their skin from the rough elements who own such animals.

(*iii*) Animals in such areas have become so clever that it is difficult to catch them single-handed. They are let loose mostly in the evening. They graze the crops in the night and then reach their destination before dawn. Day grazing is also quite common in certain areas.

(*iv*) A sort of apathy develops in the farmers and whenever the extension worker approaches them for any programme, they just say "you first solve this problem of ours and our production will automatically increase!"

The problem is both economic and social. It is economic because the cattle owners have no fodder to feed them. It is a social problem because those who leave their cattle are in most cases those persons who are undesirable elements, and therefore, farmers whose crops they graze do not dare fight with them.

What is the solution to this problem is difficult to say. But it is a problem, the solution of which is desired by every peace-loving farmer in the country. If it is not tackled effectively, it would continue to be aggravated more and more as both human and animal population continue to increase. It can be tackled mainly at the people's level with adequate governmental support. Some of the suggestions that can be given to tackle the problem are:

(*i*) Empowering *Gram Sabha* by making a provision in the *Panchayat Raj* Act to punish those who leave their

cattle to graze the crops of other farmers. In many
States such powers are already vested in the *Panchayats,* but they are not taken advantage of;

(*ii*) Setting up of an effective organisation by government
to catch and auction the stray animals;

(*ii*) Creating public opinion through a large-scale educational programme against the practice of allowing cattle to
graze about loose;

(*iv*) Popularising stall feeding;

(*v*) Educating people to keep fewer but better animals instead of a large number of animals of poor quality;

(*vi*) Castrating all the useless bulls;

(*vii*) Increasing area under fodder crops and increasing their
production;

(*viii*) Popularising the idea and practice of artificial insemination of animals;

(*ix*) Bringing eroded areas under soil and water conservation
practices and popularising cultivation of legumes, grasses
and fodder in such areas;

(*x*) Strict enforcement of the Cattle Trespass Act in cities
as well as in the rural areas.

(*xi*) Licensing and numbering of animals especially by
municipal boards, corporations, cantonments and town
areas.

In Kuthond block of Jalaun district in Uttar Pradesh, several
Gram Sabhas have solved the problem of *Anna* (*loose*) cattle
through their own efforts. People in this block and round about
the area are in the habit of leaving their cattle loose unattended
for grazing crops growing in the fields. This made improvement
of existing crops and introduction of new ones a difficult task.
Not only crops were damaged and grazed but considerable cow
dung was also wasted. In 1958-59, the District Magistrate,

Jalaun decided to popularise *moong* T. 1 crop in the month of May and June as a part of *Kharif* production campaign. He arranged for timely supply of irrigation water through the irrigation department to irrigate the crop. A plan for putting some areas under Japanese method of paddy cultivation was also prepared. A 300-acre paddy nursery was put in different areas for this purpose. Although *moong* T. 1 was sown and paddy nurseries put in, people were afraid of the loose cattle. The Shekhpur *Gram Sabha* of the block took up the challenge and passed a resolution that they will keep their cattle stall-fed and would also not allow cattle of other *Gram Sabhas* to graze in the area of their own *Gram Sabha*. If they did, they would send such cattle to cattle ponds. The *Gram Sabha* informed the neighbouring *Gram Sabhas* about this decision. It also employed two watchmen to see that no outside cattle entered their *Gram Sabha* for grazing. The concerted will of the people resulted in stopping the *Anna* practice of letting their cattle loose. The example of Shekhpur *Gram Sabha* was followed subsequently by Kherakanar, Maloopur, Neemgaon, Jamalpur and some other *Gram Sabhas* who also passed similar resolutions. Some of them also employed watchmen to enforce and to ensure controlled grazing. Some *Gram Sabhas* approached the *Zila Parishad* to open additional cattle ponds in the areas. In 1960-61 more *Gram Sabhas* of the block followed suit. These community efforts have now resulted in growing sugarcane without *kutcha* walls around the fields and in increasing area under paddy, *moong* T. 1 and cotton in the block. The income of the cattle ponds, as the result of enforcement of this decision has also increased. In 1961-62 all the *Gram Sabhas* of the block except nine stopped the *Anna* practice.

Another case history in this connection would be useful. In one *Gram Sabha* of Paraspur block of Gonda district in Uttar Pradesh, some new wells were constructed for irrigation purposes. As the result of additional irrigation facilities, the farmers desired to grow some new cash crops. They were, however, hesitant to grow them on account of the nuisance of stray cattle. The extension worker of the area thought of a new device to check this nuisance. He felt that if people were asked to stop leaving their cattle loose just in the normal course, they would not listen. He therefore, prepared a list of the bullies of the village and contacted them to try the new crops. They agreed on persuasion to sow these crops and not to leave their cattle loose for grazing. On account of the fear of these bullies who themselves agreed not to let loose their cattle for grazing, the entire *Gram Sabha* practised the same. The result was that considerable area was successfully planted in this *Gram Sabha* under new cash crops on all irrigated works. This case history shows that many a time ordinary administrative tricks also help in pushing through new programmes.

(b) Problem of wild animals and birds

They present a serious problem particularly near the forest areas where people lose considerable part of their crops due to the attack of these animals. Wild boars, blue cows, stags, monkeys and various kinds of birds are some of the common enemies of the farmer damaging the crops.

Monkeys and birds besides being a serious pest near the forest areas also do considerable damage in other areas. There is almost no control for monkeys under our conditions except catching and shooting them. Shooting is, however, not possible on account of the religious sentiments of the people. Catching and leaving them in forest area is possible, but that does not solve the problem as they come back again. Damage due to birds is checked considerably by constant watch and ward. This is, however, very expensive unless large contiguous areas are sown with a particular crop.

Wherever there is the problem of damage by the above mentioned animals, cultivation of crops like papaya, sugarcane, potato and other vegetables becomes more or less an impossibility. Introduction of these crops in such areas, therefore, does not succeed in spite of the attempts of the extension workers. Tobacco is coming to be very popular in areas where there is a serious monkey problem. This crop is not damaged by monkeys and, therefore, people find it safe to increase area under this crop wherever there is a serious monkey problem. This is specially noticeable in areas near the towns like Ayodha in Uttar Pradesh.

The problem of wild animals, particularly blue bulls and monkeys, is a great social problem under our conditions for quite a large section of the people are not inclined to kill them. The damage due to these animals can only be stopped if the religious sentiments of the people are gradually changed and public opinion in favour of killing these animals is created.

(c) *Problem of water-logging and drainage*

Of late, the problem of water-logging is becoming very acute due to large scale construction of bunds, canals, railway lines, flood protection enbankments and changed pattern of rainfall coming in incessant downpours. The area under water-logging is constantly increasing. What were before high yielding areas are now almost turning into saline or alkaline areas with very little production.

The problem of water-logging is becoming so acute that people do not like to adopt new programmes for fear of loss of their crops. The situation can be improved only by providing proper drainage and changing the existing rotations with new ones.

(d) *Problem of uncertain supplies of irrigation water*

This is also a very serious problem in Uttar Pradesh and several other States where a large number of State irrigation works have been constructed. Irrigation around most of these State irrigation works has been planned with a view to providing maximum benefit to the largest number of persons and areas. As consciousness for increasing agricultural production is developing in the people, the demand for irrigation water is also increasing enormously with the result that the aim of benefiting the largest area and number of persons is becoming difficult to be fulfilled. This is reflected in innumerable complaints that cultivators and field workers are making against the untimely and insufficient supply of water. The evaluation of *Kharif* and *Rabi* production campaigns in 1958-59 in Uttar Pradesh carried out by the Director. Planning Research and Action Institute, Lucknow (U.P.), has also brought out this fact clearly as would appear from the following figures collected in this connection:

Type of respondents interviewed.	Kharif Campaign		Rabi Campaign	
	Percentage of respondents who complained.	Number of respondents who complained.	Percentage of respondents who complained.	Number of respondents who complained.
(*i*) Village level campaigners:				
a) Active blocks	47.0	63	55.14	49
b) Shadow blocks.	43.3	13	64.29	13
(*ii*) Block level officer.	—	—	81.50	130
(*iii*) Farmers or village leaders:				
a) Active blocks	70.2	399	55.19	202
b) Shadow blocks.			63.10	65

The above figures show that irrigation is one of the major problems causing anxiety to cultivators. In the face of this pressing anxiety the removal of which does not seem to be in sight, the farmers whenever they are approached by an extension worker retort by saying, "you give us water for irrigation and we will do all that you want us to do". With this attitude of the farmers, the extension worker also finds it difficult to suggest new programmes to the cultivators. Several crops which could be raised if sufficient quantity of water was available, cannot possibly be introduced. Various improved crop rotations which are once popularised, have to be given up by the farmers, next year for want of assured supply of water. In the circumstances, when supplies are irregular and uncertain, cultivators remain wavering in their minds about the future programmes and thus hesitate in adopting new ones. This can be solved only if, in such areas, the farmers are encouraged to supplement their own smaller minor irrigation works making intensive cultivation possible. Another alternative is to reduce the command area, but this step is likely to increase discontentment because the farmers who are already enjoying some benefit would not like to be deprived of it.

(5) *Programme planning*

Programme planning is a process which includes the following:

(*a*) Selection of programmes based upon careful analysis of the factual situation in respect of soil, the people, the community and its organisations, customs, beliefs, traditions, *etc.,* and the existing technical, economic and social level of the people and their special needs.

(*b*) Development of a plan of work to enable efficient execution of the programme.

The selection of programmes answers the questions like—What is the problem, what should be done and why? It includes the following steps:

(*a*) Collection, analysis and the evaluation of all available factual information bearing upon the welfare of the families and community.

(*b*) Determination of the objectives based upon the need of the community.

(*c*) Definition of the objectives.

(*d*) Finding solutions to problems and deciding upon the programmes to solve them.

The plan of work tells, how, when and where and by whom the programme shall be carried out. It also consists of many steps. These are discussed in detail under the heading 'Action Programme' on pages 152 and 153 of the book, and are, therefore, not given here.

Careful planning of extension programme is necessary:

(1) To concentrate efforts on achieving the objective.

(2) To keep the extension worker and the people on the track without involving them in trivialities.

(3) To make the most effective use of the available resources of land, labour, capital, human material and time.

(4) To provide for continuity of efforts towards the accomplishment of the objectives in case the personnel changes.

(5) To time the utilisation of resources in a way that both short and long-term objectives are achieved.

Proper programme planning is essential for successful extension of programmes. It is, however, often neglected. There are various reasons for its neglect. It would be useful to enumerate them below:

(1) There is an attempt to solve too many problems or take up too many programmes at the same time without making any significant contribution to any of them. Care has to be taken to select only important items for paying attention to in any particular year or period. These items should be such as to give immediate relief or satisfaction to the people. Side by side with such programmes, a beginning should also be made to take up some basic problems or programmes requiring a longer period of time for completion but which are otherwise important and have a bearing upon the welfare of the people.

(2) Haste in showing quick results.

(3) Frequent changes in the programmes by the senior workers or officers.

(4) Starting of overlapping programmes in the shape of drives.

(5) Lack of proper training of the workers and the village leaders in programme planning.

(6) Belief on the part of senior workers that issuing of the mere instructions is enough to get the job done.

(7) Too much emphasis on achieving short-term results.

Programme planning is a very effective progress of education of the workers as well as of the people provided it is democratically carried out with their consultation. It helps to bring about a change in their thinking and develops an ability to solve their own problems individually or collectively. It teaches people to collect and analyse things and take a decision about the time of the action to be adopted. It tells them how to co-operate to achieve a common objective and how to meet new problems and new situations as they arise.

Not only programme planning should be carried out democratically but all subsequent decisions concerning execution and evaluation should also be democratically taken at a meeting. If at any time, it becomes necessary to modify the plan of action, it should be done in consultation with the workers and the people.

Plans may have to be changed frequently because new problems and situations keep coming up.

(i) Present trends

Late Prime Minister Nehru in one of his frank appraisals of the working of the Plans observed: "There is a tendency in all of us to sit in offices and draw up plans and to ignore a very vital aspect of our problem. We talk lightly of hundreds of thousands of crores. These figures have no meaning to the peasant, nor is he greatly impressed by stories of mighty river-valley schemes, steel plants, *etc.*, which do not directly affect him. What impresses him is what he sees round about. Therefore, it is better for us to lay stress on a large number of small schemes for irrigation purposes and small industries. These will require relatively little capital and will bring forth results within a few months. The farmer can see them growing up and can appreciate the benefits which he derives from them. That is why we are now thinking more of variety of minor schemes spread out all over the country. This leads to a more balanced development of the country and helps in training up our people and making them understand modern methods. This programme of having relatively small schemes can be applied to production of fertilizers and of pig-iron. I am not running down big schemes for, I think, they are vital to our task, but I do appeal for a multitude of small schemes now which will bring all our planning to the eyes of the farmer".

These observations of Mr. Nehru about finalising plans in the office without involving the people concerned, apply with great force to programme planning in National Extension Movement also. The result of all this is that the people do not feel a party to them. Quite a number of Plans generally do not suit them as they do not fit in the local conditions and fail to make an appeal to the people. In some cases the Plans are too complicated to be followed by the people. Often the programmes are just ordered to be implemented. Such orders result in the majority of cases in superficial work. In good number of cases, the workers themselves do not feel convinced about the programme but they just try to execute it because they have been ordered to do so. Simply for fear of reprimand, they try to show some achievement here and there. As soon as the person ordering the execution of the programme is transferred or he shifts his emphasis to another programme on account of a new brain wave or due to some compelling circumstances, the pressure on its implementation is relaxed and it fizzles out. Whatever achievement had been there, is lost in oblivion.

Programme planning is a means to achieve an objective. It should never become an end in itself. When it becomes an end through wrong emphasis, its educational purpose is lost. This is at present happening in the matter of preparation of village and farm production plans of the individual farmers. Instead of carrying it out as an educational process to change their thinking and break old traditions and replace them with the new, plan-making is becoming more or less a mechanical process of filling pro forma to complete the target fixed for preparing farm production plans and providing co-operative credit. Although some good might come out from such mechanical working the main objective would not be achieved even though targets in respect of co-operative credit and preparation of farm production plans were achieved.

A common mistake committed is the issuing of general instructions for adoption of programmes, hoping that they would be applicable to all conditions. This is a wrong notion for no instructions however perfect, can be applicable to all local conditions and situations. The basic principles being the same, latitude should always be given to workers to modify them to suit the requirements of the area which differ not only from state to state but also from district to district, block to block, village to village and even in a particular village from field to field. Programmes, therefore, have to be selected locally within the overall frame of objective according to their applicability to the local conditions. Instructions were issued in a certain State of the country in 1958-59 by its agriculture department to all the districts and blocks growing paddy to popularise line sowing followed by the application of fertilisers and interculture in the crop to replace the practice of broadcasting which gave low yield per acre. The workers started following these instructions, but they failed at many places and ultimately gave up the practice as unsuitable. The practice could have been introduced in most of the areas, by making modifications to suit local conditions but the workers did not feel competent to modify the instructions received from higher quarters.

The practice of line sowing in paddy was afterwards found to succeed in this State under the following conditions only:

1. In irrigated, well-drained, light soils, provided sowing was carried out before the monsoon.

2. In deep-water paddy areas, provided sowing was carried out during the months from March to May.

3. In areas where light rain falls early or even up to end of June and seed is able to germinate before heavy rains come.

4. In Bhat soils which are very retentive of moisture and are sown before rains.

It has been found to fail:

1. If sowing was carried out after the 2nd week of July.

2. In heavy soils when sowing was done with the onset of rains.

The above example would show that, howsoever, simple a programme may appear, it has different implications in different soil and climatic conditions. If programmes like this are made applicable to every area, by issuing some kind of general executive instructions, they fail at places and thus give a very wrong impression to the farmers on whose fields they fail. They are also subsequently not tried and taken up by other farmers when they notice their failure at one place.

Yet another unhealthy tendency that is growing is to discuss programmes in conferences and meetings and take *ad hoc* decisions without going into the details of such decisions. In one high-powered conference, a decision was taken that all cultivated areas should be supplied with at least two tons of compost per acre. It was a herculean task, the difficulties of which were not thought of at the time of making the recommendations. As soon as the conference was over, the decision was conveyed to all the State Governments for implementation. Several State Governments reported that instructions had been issued to all the

Block Development Officers for compliance. The decision taken was thus given a decent burial. Nobody knew or bothered about what the Block Development Officers did with the recommendation. They in turn passed on the same to village level workers in the staff meetings. The village level workers being baffled by its impracticability, forgot about it. This is what happens with several recommendations which are made in conferences and meetings without going into their details. Any recommendation that is made, should be thoroughly considered and analysed before and after it is made. It should be followed with proper programme planning before it is accepted by the people for whose benefit it is meant.

(ii) Remedy

The remedy for such a faulty attitude lies in taking up only a few programmes at a time, preparing detailed plans for their execution, training the staff in proper programme planning before starting the work, and reviewing their progress from time to time.

Quality and quantity of work within certain limits are mutually exclusive of each other. Both are important, but if either suffers abnormally, the result is unfavourable. If 'quality' is maintained, in the long run it helps to increase 'quantity' in geometrical progression. If on the other hand, there is too much stress on 'quantity' in the beginning, 'quality' suffers. The increased 'quantity' is progressively reduced after some time to a negligible quantity resulting in reversal to the original state. Quality in work should, therefore, be given greater stress than quantity and once a tempo is created, and people become convinced of the programme, quantity of the quality programme would automatically increase in a surprising manner.

(6) Approaching people for adoption of programmes

There are generally five kinds of approaches followed by extension workers for adoption of the programmes by the people. These are:

(i) Obligation approach;

(ii) Imposition or authoritarian approach;

   (*iii*) Financial or inducement approach;

   (*iv*) Reliance approach;

   (*v*) Educational approach.

(*i*) Obligation approach

The extension worker in this approach generally contacts those whom he knows from before. Such persons consent to try the recommended programme just to oblige him irrespective of the fact whether they believe in it or not. Such an obligation is repaid by the extension worker in the form of some economic or social benefit.

Approaching such individuals (who are generally well to do persons), results in temporary and sometimes in the permanent adoption of a programme by them. Usually, they are the ones who are pioneers in the adoption of a new programme. They readily adopt the programme thinking that it might turn out to be something very profitable for them. Sometimes they adopt it for showing their importance to other villagers for if the programme is new and promising, the extension worker tries to bring round important visitors to show their implementation. This creates a feeling of self-importance in them. Some of these persons also readily consent to arrange feast or parties in honour of the visiting dignitaries at the instance of extension worker who has to put up a show to please his immediate superiors. A good deal of money is spent on such entertainments and ceremonies by the obliger. He later on tries to seek himself, if he is empowered to do so, or helps to get them from his officers, in order to have a few such individuals always at his beck and call. After a lapse of time, such individuals surround the extension workers like a shadow and very often, they are the ones who greet a visitor, as soon as he reaches a block or a village.

Approach of this kind leads to very little extension of the programmes, but to a sort of false picture in which everything appears to be moving well but nothing or very little moves actually. Continued approach on this line becomes a racket of its kind from which it becomes difficult to get out.

There are numerous examples of such situations. For instance a high ranking officer was very fond of popularising the cultivation of bananas. Whenever he went on tour, he wanted to see the progress of this programme in the villages. Noticing his unusual keeness, all officers under him saw to it that on all roads leading to village sites and near houses, drains, wells, *etc.,* banana-suckers were planted before he arrived. The result was that opportunist leaders in the villages on the express desire of the official workers planted banana-suckers about a few hours before the arrival of this officer at all sorts of places just to impress the visitor. Most of these suckers dried after four or five days. When this officer was transferred, it was noticed that the villages he had visited, had a lesser number of banana plants than while he was posted to the district.

All the junior officers during such visits of the dignitary felt obliged to their immediate subordinate officers or workers and the village leaders who helped to make his visit a success. The higher officers had to return the obligation in some form or the other. Although the obligations were exchanged for mutual advantage after the visit, the programme did not make any headway as most of the banana plants were utilised in putting up the show to please the officer. Success in such programmes consists mainly in pleasing the officer and not in pushing the programme.

(ii)   Imposition or authoritarian approach

In this approach, the worker induces the people to adopt a certain programme about which they have not been educated or convinced and may even be suspicious. This approach is more common with untrained administrative officers whether technical or executive rather than officers trained in extension work. As almost all the extension programmes in India are run under the overall supervision of the administrative officers there are several occasions when this kind of approach is resorted to by the workers. Imposition of programmes in many cases results in their adoption also, but such an adoption is mainly temporary and lasts till the official pressure or insistence is maintained. There can also be some instances of permanent adoption of programmes in this kind of approach, but such an adoption is there only when the imposition is continued for sufficiently long till it becomes a habit with them.

This kind of approach deprives the people of their self-motivation. The people adopt the programme because of the order or compulsion and not due to their belief in its efficacy.

(iii) Financial or inducement approach

In this approach, the extension worker tries to get programmes executed through the promises of some financial aid. The quantum of financial aid varies according to the programmes and the general condition of the people. The aid is generally more for backward areas or communities than progressive areas or communities. Several government-sponsored schemes are run on this basis. The idea behind this aid is to initiate people to undertake some programmes with their own resources supplemented by the State resources. It is expected that after the programmes are initiated, people would be able to shoulder the responsibility of continuing these programmes.

Financial approach, although expected to result in enthusing people, does not in the majority of cases leave the people genuinely enthused for taking up future responsibilities. If the aid has been provided in the budget, they feel, it is their right and, therefore, they press their claim for it. As the aid depends upon the matching contribution from the receiver, there are more chances that only those who are well to do get the aid. Those who do not have any resources or have meagre resources do not get such aids. Aid being dependent upon the local contribution, results in a tendency to inflate the estimates for getting a bigger amount. This tendency causes more harm than good because the very purpose of giving aid is defeated.

A few years back, free fertilizers were supplied to Block Development Officers for carrying out demonstrations and testing the efficacy of some new fertilizers. Many extension workers tagged this free supply of fertilizers with some other programmes which they wanted to popularise. The result was that the people who were supplied with these fertilizers, did apply them and also got good results, but they did not like to purchase them next year. They waited for the extension worker to give them these fertilizers once again free of cost. Total or partial financial aid in such circumstances becomes in itself a hindrance to the extension of programmes.

Financial aid should be given very cautiously. As far as possible, aid should be given in kind not in cash, and only for those items which people cannot easily manage through their own resources.

Financial approach in agricultural and community development programmes is sometimes necessary, but nevertheless detrimental in the long run in the interest of the programmes themselves. This may not be the rule but it is true of most of the programmes which take root and spread faster if they are initiated with the people's own resources or with financial aid only after they have been properly enthused and initiated to action.

(iv) Reliance approach

Under this approach, the worker tries to develop such an atmosphere that every one in the village believes in him and in his *bonafides* so that whatever he says is believed and adopted by the people. This kind of approach is not common. Whenever this method has been followed, the adoption of programmes by the people is easier, quicker and is based on their conviction. Some workers have a religious bent of mind and are fond of reciting the *Ramayan* and other religious books with fervour. Such workers are generally popular in the villages. People in the course of time develop faith in them and become prepared to do anything suggested to them.

(v) Educational approach

This is the real approach all the extension workers must adopt. This approach takes considerable time to succeed and requires patience but is effective in the long run. It consists of:

(1) Stimulating a process of thinking which may enable the people to spot out real problems and take action in respect of them;

(2) Imparting knowledge and skill about programmes; and

(3) Involving the people to make their own plans incorporating their own suggestions based on local experience.

Actual demonstrations and study tours result in motivating the people to take up responsibility of executing the programme shown to them for they come to believe in its efficacy and suitability before they accept it.

Although educational approach is the best of all approaches, it becomes impossible to continue with it in the present conditions howsoever the workers may try to adhere to it. This is because a good many programmes carry a rider that they should be executed within a specified time. In such circumstances, extension workers do not stick to this approach but prefer to follow the first two approaches lest they should incur displeasure of the seniors.

Occasionally an attempt is made to impose a programme. This imposition starts from the top who feels itself competent enough to take a decision and thrust it down below without consulting the workers through whom the decision is to be implemented or the people for whose benefit the decision is supposed to have been made. The decision in the shape of an order is passed down, stage by stage to the lowest wrung of the ladder where it is received with misgivings and even bitterness by the workers as well as the people. Each one in the official hierarchy feels that he is dictated by the one who is higher up. The people in fact, are the real master and unless they are properly educated first and enthused to plan out their own programmes with the help of the official agency, there can be no real or lasting success. It is not enough that they have their representatives in the State Assemblies or in the Parliament or in various committees constituted by government. It is necessary that they should have full hand in planning things for themselves and taking initiative in all programmes benefiting them. To associate them, with a view to making them feel responsible for their own welfare, needs an educational approach towards development programmes. No official machinery, at whatever level it may be, can afford to ignore this aspect. Even a dictator like Napolean who conquered countries after countries in his life by brute force, is said to have admitted before his death at St. Helena that no permanent improvement could be brought about in human life by force or threat of violence. It is only through the educational approach that the people can be encouraged to move forward.

Of all the five approaches, educational approach is the best and should be invariably followed. It is, however, not possible to follow only one approach on all occasions. In some situations, it may be necessary to use more than one approach. An approach to the people by obliging them through financial aid or by justifying to impose things on them under some sort of pressure or the other cannot lead to any lasting and abiding results. This has been demonstrated in the past with a number of projects which were supposed to induce farmers to make improvements. On the other hand, working directly with the people, educating them and winning their confidence and developing their understanding and thinking helps to create a lasting interest in developmental activities and an urge for betterment.

CHAPTER III

THE ATTITUDE AND OUTLOOK
OF THE OFFICIAL MACHINERY

1. *Proper approach*

APPROACH TO agricultural and community development programmes and problems of the people depends to a great extent upon the attitude and outlook of the immediate and senior
officers and the workers at all levels. If the approach at the
top is promotional, it filters down to the intermediate supervisory links who also react to it. Under ideal conditions, the
approach from the top down should be of this nature, but such
an ideal condition is difficult to get and can only be possible
if all the workers from the top down are properly trained in
extension methods and believe in their efficacy.

Training of all personnel—big or small—for manning the programmes is necessary before they are started. Training a few
and not training others and starting the programme is no doubt
a step forward in the right direction, but it ultimately affects
even the performance of the trained workers because of lack of
sufficient understanding and receptivity on the part of others.
This happened with the community development programme in
India where subordinate workers were thoroughly trained at the
time of its start in 1952 but not their senior ones. Although
this deficiency was realised later, but it was too late in the day
because the programme by then, had already expanded a great
deal making it impossible to post all trained workers in a project
simultaneously. It is difficult to say that the programme would

93

have assumed a different shape if all the workers in 1952 right from the District Magistrate to the Village Level Worker in the district selected for the programme had been properly trained for the job and given necessary orientation.

2. *Composition of the official machinery*

Some machinery already existed in the country before the start of the community development programme in 1952. It varied in composition from State to State and was more or less of the following order in different States of the country:

(a) *At the village level*:

(i) *Panchayat* Secretary (In some States only).
(ii) Village *Panchayat* with its executive committees (in most of the States).
(iii) Co-operative Supervisor and *Kamdar*.
(iv) Village Co-operative Society with its Board of Directors.
(v) Agriculture Supervisor and *Kamdar*.
(vi) Cane Supervisor and *Kamdar* (In some States only).
(vii) Stockman.
(viii) School teacher.
(ix) Zone worker—*Prantiya Rakshak Dal* (In Uttar Pradesh only).

(b) *At the Tehsil or Taluka level*:

(i) Agriculture Inspector.
(ii) Co-operative Inspector.
(iii) Veterinary Assistant Surgeon.
(iv) *Panchayat* Inspector.
(v) Sub-Deputy Inspector of Schools.
(vi) Sanitary Inspector.

(c) *At the District level*:

(i) District Magistrate.
(ii) District Planning Officer (in some States only).
(iii) Team of district level technical officers with their staff.
(iv) District Planning Committee with its executive committees.

(*d*) *At the regional level*:

    (*i*) Commissioner of the Division.
    (*ii*) Deputy/Assistant Development Commissioner.
    (*iii*) Team of technical officers of Development Departments with their staff.
    (*iv*) Zonal Development Committee.

(*e*) *At the State level*:

    (*i*) Development Commissioner.
    (*ii*) Team of technical heads of departments with their staff.
    (*iii*) Deputy/Assistant Development Commissioners.
    (*iv*) State Co-ordination Committee.
    (*v*) State Development Board.

The community development programme, when it was started in 1952, was considered to be an integrated and co-ordinated programme of emotional integration, socio-economic change and personality development of the people. Its basic aim was to create in them a desire and an aspiration for a new and better way of life, to develop self-confidence and habits of co-operation and initiative for undertaking responsibility for their welfare upon themselves.

The programme needed some additional agency besides the existing agency to initiate and bring about a change. This machinery consisted of:

(a) *At the village level*:

    (*i*) Village Level Worker.
    (*ii*) *Gram Sevikas.*
    (*iii*) *Gram Lakshmis.*
    (*iv*) *Dais.*

(b) *At the block level*:

    (*i*) Block Development Officer.
    (*ii*) Team of subject-matter specialists.
    (*iii*) Block Development Committee with its executive committees (now *Kshetra Samitis*).

It would appear from the above that most of the machinery existed from before. The important addition that was made was the multi-purpose workers, *Gram Sevikas, Gram Lakshmis* and *Dais* at the village level, and the Block Development Officer, with a team of subject-matter specialists and a block development committee consisting of mainly non-officials to advise at the block level. These were very important additions, as due to them, the level of administration was, for the first time decentralised from the *Tehsil* or *Taluka* to a small, manageable administrative unit called a block thus bringing the government machinery nearer to the people than before. At the block level, the entire staff was placed under the Block Development Officer, thus providing for an unified command with a clear-cut programme and funds easily available within easy reach of the people.

The entire machinery given above was governmental but at all levels, people were associated in advisory capacity through local committees or bodies like block development committee, district planning committee, state development board, zonal planning committee, *etc.* Association of the people in advisory capacity at the district level and below has now been recently replaced in almost all the States of the country with their direct responsibility in which they have been made fully responsible for execution of all rural programmes in the district. The district planning committee and the district boards have now given place to *Zila Parishads* and block development committees to *Kshetra Samitis*. The responsibility of execution of these programmes at these levels is now of the *Adhyaksh* (Chairman) of *Zila Parishad* and *Pramukhs* of *Kshetra Samitis* with the District Planning Officer and the Block Development Officer serving as their respective executive officers. The technical officers at these levels work under the District Planning Officer and the Block Development Officer respectively. This is a very big change and has for the first time placed the responsibility for execution of programmes on the shoulders of the representatives of the people—*panchayat* in the village, the *panchayat samiti* consisting of the *Mukhiyas* or the representatives of the *panchayats* at the block, and the *Zila Parishad* at the district level supervising the work of the *panchayats* and the *panchayat samitis.* The three-tier process of democratic decentralisation has for the first time widened the base of administration by providing a right kind of structure to our democracy.

The official machinery at these levels instead of working as a governmental agency is now working under the direction of the representatives of the people with some indirect governmental control. This means complete change in the outlook of the official machinery.

3. *Training of the machinery*

The attitude and approach of the official machinery depends upon :

(*a*) The inherent qualities of the individual members.

(*b*) Effect of the process of socialisation of the society on the individual.

(*c*) Effect of pre-service and in-service training.

(*d*) Guidance provided by the seniors.

The individuals join the family of the official machinery after (*a*) and (*b*) stages are over. Whatever changes in their attitudes and approach can be made by the employer after screening them through a selection board, are possible only through pre-service and in-service training and guidance from seniors and colleagues. Training, thus, plays a very important part in moulding the worker. This was realised by the authorities sponsoring the community development programme and therefore, several centres were simultaneously opened to train the personnel at the time of starting the programme. The pace of training programme was, however, not maintained as fast as the coverage of the area with the community development programme with the result that both trained and untrained workers worked together in the same project.

The main emphasis in the training was laid on changing the attitudes, behaviours and outlook of the trainees towards the rural programmes and the people besides imparting technical knowledge. The main principles behind the training were as below :

5

(*i*) That the community development programme was an educational programme for initiating a desire for change in the people, and then enabling them to bring about that change.

(*ii*) The governmental machinery at all levels—block, district, region, State and also Centre—was to work as a team with a co-operative and integrated outlook for all problems. All the decisions were to be taken by the team as a whole and not by the senior-most officer alone.

This was expected to give a feeling of partnership to the worker at all levels in the programme.

(*iii*) Development of sympathetic and democratic outlook to all problems and difficulties of the people.

(*iv*) Association and approval of the people or their representatives in all decisions affecting them.

(*v*) Discontinuance of the traditional boss-subordinate relationship to that of equal partnership in planning and solving all problems arising in the field through mutual discussions and consultations in a spirit of give and take by teaching and learning from each other.

(*vi*) Replacement of the traditional supervisory attitude by the desire to make a close study of problems with a view to guiding the personnel and the people.

(*vii*) Creation of a sense of urgency for taking quick decisions in all matters.

(*viii*) Having faith in the *bonafides* of the extension worker with a view to building him up by constructive guidance.

(*ix*) A sympathetic approach towards the people in order to be a friend and a guide.

(*x*) Holding of regular staff meetings to review the progress achieved, to remove doubts and difficulties of the workers, to allow free and frank discussions and to finalise programme of work for the next period.

(*xi*) Need of periodical evaluation of the programme from time to time by the extension workers themselves alone and in consultation with the people and making necessary changes and adjustments in them to suit local conditions including social, cultural and economic conditions of the people.

4. *Trained workers in action*

The workers trained to believe in the above principles when posted to 1952 and 1953 series of Community Project blocks were so imbued with the new thinking that immediately after about six months of their posting in the area, a change was noticeable in the attitudes of the people. They started treating the extension staff as their friend, saviour and well-wisher so much so that they even came and complained to them about the excesses and malpractices committed by the police, *Lekhpal* (village record keeper), Sanitary Inspector and other government servants and sought their help for redress. The old machinery in the existing blocks felt shaky and started non-co-operating with the project staff because its staff stood in sharp contrast with that of another organisation of government in whom the people started reposing confidence. It also started complaining against this staff to the District Magistrate who was the common boss for them. In districts where the District Magistrate appreciated the change in the people, they helped and supported the project staff and its programme but in others in which this change was not appreciated, things went without attracting the District Magistrate's notice.

The change that came as a result of the impact of these trained personnel was so apparent that it immediately caught the imagination of the politicians as one of the important programmes which could bring about an economic and social revolution in the country leading to a socialistic pattern of society.

5. *Programme allowed to expand*

This led to the expansion of the programme faster than the pace at which trained personnel could be made available to man the programme. Already some of the workers in the existing blocks and the districts including the District Magistrates and the district level officers, where the community development programme was in operation were untrained. To this list was added the staff of the new blocks with the result that the programme at the block level was manned both by the trained and untrained staff with the senior officers also not trained or only partially trained.

6. *Defects that followed due to large and quick expansion*

Several defects and complications appeared as the result of this unmanageable expansion. Some important ones among these are discussed here.

(*i*) The programme had to be manned by untrained staff sometimes of low calibre.

(*ii*) Supervision and guidance from the district, region and State level so necessary in the early stages were not so effective as they should have been and they became sporadic instead of being regular and sustained.

(*iii*) On account of expansion, the need was felt to decentralise more and more powers from the State headquarters to the Divisional Commissioners, regional officers, District Magistrates and other district level officers who were made responsible for the execution of the programme at their levels. The Block Development Officer thus had in the course of time several bosses both in the administrative as well as in the technical line to whom he looked for orders and guidance. Most of the senior officers were not trained in extension methods, but in spite of this, the responsibility of guiding and executing the programme was entrusted to them. The approach of most of them was authoritarian, bureaucratic and impersonal.

(*iv*) Most of the technical officers at the district level felt frustrated due to their being placed under a District Planning Officer[9] an officer of almost equal rank. Some of the district planning officers did not have confidence in themselves and felt diffident in giving practical spot guidance to block development officers. Just because they had more intimate contact with the field and the people, the block development officers felt that they knew more than the district level technical officers. The administrative machinery at the district, regional and also at the State level noticed lack of interest on the part of the technical officers and concluded that the technical machinery was incompetent and unable to deliver the goods. The technical machinery on the other hand, having a feeling of inferiority and sense of frustration also

[9] This officer is available in only a few States.

felt the same way about the administrative machinery. As it had been placed under the executive machinery, it adopted an attitude of get-going and started obeying the executive machinery mechanically as a dumb creature without any initiative or spirit of guidance on their part.

(v) The Ministry of Community Development in the meantime started insisting that technical departments should be given full responsibility of executing their programmes in the blocks. When these instructions filtered down to the field, it gave a feeling to the technical officers in the regions that the block was now the agency for executing programmes and that their duty was only to issue orders and expect compliance from the block development officers through their district level officers. Instructions issued from the headquarters were thus mechanically passed on to the regional officers and from them to the district officers and so on to the block development officers and village level workers. This machinery also coupled with the existing administrative machinery started ordering things to be done by the project workers without taking into consideration whether the programmes suited their areas or not or whether or not necessary supplies, for expanding the scope of the programme were available.

(vi) As the result of all this, the original concept of the community development programme was lost sight of. It no longer remained an educational programme although the professed aim is still the same. It became a bureaucratic affair mostly undertaken in the shape of short-term pressure drives without any follow-up. The programmes were executed as per order without taking into consideration the changes required to suit local conditions. This resulted mostly in poor response to the programmes. They were rejected in many cases by the official machinery itself as unsuitable to the area although they could be suitable with proper adjustments and changes.

(vii) A special type of boss-subordinate relationship started to develop. It became a hindrance in the extension of programmes. The subordinates at all levels in this kind of relationship followed the course of least resistance. They tried to adapt them-

selves to all that the boss said without real and intelligent participation or without taking into account local conditions or situations. Even if the programme did not suit the area, they did
not resist the idea for fear of incurring the displeasure of
the higher officers. Directives from the headquarters were
regarded as having a special sanctity which cannot or should not
be modified. As promotions and prospects depended upon the
goodwill of the higher officers, a tendency to toe the dictated
line developed, and as the result the subordinates at all levels
remained more oriented towards their higher officers than towards
the people whom they were meant to serve. A circle of four or
five petty officials generally develops around a boss, and they
become his advisers and critics of others.

(*viii*) Some subordinates do try to modify the programme to
suit local conditions. If such modifications succeed, the subordinates are valued by the officers and their initiative is praised.
If, however, the modification fails, the subordinates try to hide
it from their bosses. The experience of failure of the modification is thus in many cases not shared with the boss for fear
lest one should be looked down upon and thus one remained
ignorant about the field experience.

(*ix*) The programmes are undertaken as short-lived pressure
drives with prescribed time-limit and almost complete absence
of follow-up. The short-lived drives follow one after another for
one item or the other belonging to the same department or different departments and thus the workers do not get time to think
and consolidate the gains of the previous drive. Supervision
from higher ups is sporadic and not continuous. This results in
the old work becoming mostly redundant, except for a few temporary physical achievements without any or much impact on the
people. The programmes in most of these cases do not take
roots.

(*x*) Programmes which require patient and sustained efforts
over a long period are attempted to be done in a hurry. Vast
sums are spent in attempting to achieve quick results in spheres
which require long and persistent efforts. If quick results are
not achieved, programmes are given up as failures and are

substituted by new programmes without analysing the causes of failures.

(*xi*) High sounding names are many times given to new programmes without realising that they cannot make up for the inherent deficiencies in them. Old things are replaced by implanting new ones just on the whims of a high dignitary. A propaganda is whipped through the press glorifying the programmes and the originator. This goes on for some time and then the whole campaign dies down or is set aside by another which amounts to changing horses in mid-stream. Thus the cycle goes on.

Creation of new things without caring to improve the old leads to new expenditure and new responsibilities and allows the old to linger on unattended and uncared for, resulting in improper utilisation and wastage of the existing resources.

(*xii*) A tendency to lay more stress on visible accomplishments and completion of the physical targets develops when targets are not completed. This results in exaggerated and false reporting. Some officers are in the habit of getting telegraphic reports. Sometimes these reports are asked for every tenth or fifteenth day without taking into consideration whether a worker can possibly send such reports and yet maintain the tempo of the programme. A certain officer asked for progress reports of the work done every tenth day. The report too consisted of seven to eight pages. It was not possible for the workers to send these reports. They, however, did send them for if anybody did not, he was warned. The result of this was that workers felt demoralised and started sending false reports. No worker, however, dared tell the officer that he should not ask for the ten-day reports as it dislocated the work in the field. If anybody made any suggestion, it was not relished.

Asking for progress reports too frequently dislocates the work. It may be practical to send such reports for institutions like banks where the day's work is closed finally. But it is not practical where the work is spread over several villages and it consists of several programmes and a large number of men are involved in implementing it. Progress reports on such works should not be called for earlier than a month and better it would be to call them quarterly or six-monthly. Too frequent reports take too much time of the workers and the officer himself, distract their minds, result in greater expenditure of stationery, require more office staff to compile them, demoralise the workers and compel them to cook up such reports.

(*xiii*) Many officers come to believe in some schemes, which become their favourite. When the officers are transferred, their successors set aside these schemes by giving a low priority and start their favourite schemes. Transfers of officers and staff are becoming frequent on account of political and other pressures. As the result of it there is no follow-up and continuity of the programme is disturbed.

(*xiv*) A tendency to show superficial achievements is developing. If this thinking is present in the senior bosses, it also filters downwards to the lower level. This tendency has increased so much that it has filtered down even to the level of *Gram Sabha* Presidents and other local leaders. Such a tendency of impressing visitors by the show put up for them is definitely wrong and leads to considerable demoralisation of workers as well as the people concerned. Sometimes demonstration of superficial achievements becomes a prestige issue with the *Gram Panchayat* or the block and in such cases, the means adopted to make up the show are very often not above board. Use of unfair means in showing of programmes spoils the worker and creates in him the tendency to exhibit made up things to the same officer who expected him to arrange showy things to please his senior officers.

(*xv*) There is hardly any sense of urgency in dealing with the programmes of the people. Sense of urgency is visible only in such matters as the boss is interested in and shows his preference for. The bosses are concerned with what their hierarchically superior bosses are most interested in. If the boss becomes interested in the small saving drive, the whole machinery from the top to bottom becomes interested in it and tries to please the boss by trying to achieve targets in time. The targets of small savings fixed by several State governments in the country were more than achieved on the last day of a particular year (March 31), but 80 to 90 per cent of this money which was deposited between

March 15 and 31 was withdrawn within a week or two after March 31. This happened because undue pressure and irregular means were used for completing the target. Very often it is forgotten that even when there is a sense of urgency, targets could be achieved by broad-basing the programme and starting it in a way that the people become a party to it.

As already described, the urgency, if any, is in most cases limited to what the senior officer is most interested in. Most of the other work is relegated by them to a later date even though it is urgent from the standpoint of the people or the programme. Such indifference and low priority to the programmes as compared with the wish of the boss in due course of time brings about an unwelcome change in the attitude of the workers towards the programme and the people.

(*xvi*) The programme is carried out as if it was just an official programme. The staff tries to assume the leadership itself. This leadership is not enduring, and it does not give a feeling of confidence to the people. This is because this leadership caters more for the wishes of the bosses than the people whom they are expected to serve.

(*xvii*) Programmes are generally conceived at higher levels without discussion with the people and are ordered to be executed in a particular way. Orders issue from the highest to the next subordinate authority, from the latter to its next and so on till they are received by the workers at the lowest level in the hierarchy. The latter are thus the persons who have to execute the orders. They have in most cases no say except to obey and execute orders even though they feel that these orders do not suit their areas.

One very able principal of a village level workers' training centre in one of the leading States of the country told me once that the number of programmes to follow in the field has now become so large and instructions about them so voluminous that he had given up seeing as to what was applicable in his area and what was not. He had started executing instructions as best as he could almost mechanically and in consequence he had lost the practice of giving thought to the applicability of programmes to the area.

(*xviii*) The departments have of late, become very critical of the community development programme. Every one of them almost invariably has a view that the block agency is not devoting adequate attention to their programmes. This criticism is leading to a lot of frustration and embittered feelings in the block staff. Much of this criticism is due to inadequate understanding, appreciation and co-ordinated approach about the problems of the block staff responsible for executing programmes of several departments which in many cases are not able to provide necessary guidance and facilities of supplies, credit, *etc.*, as and when required due to their own departmental bottlenecks, procedures and policies. In the majority of the cases, only targets are fixed, orders are issued and compliance is expected, whether it is possible or not. If there is inadequate or imperfect compliance as is usually the case in such circumstances, there is criticism open or whispering, on both the sides. How can the targets be achieved in these circumstances? How can the people be educated in the programme, if the educators themselves are not fully equipped with practical knowledge about the programmes? The result is obvious.

(*xix*) In a bid to please superiors there is a tendency to boost up figures. There is no adequate machinery to check these figures and if there is any, it seldom tries to check it for fear of unnecessary administrative complications. The result is that there is a marked tendency towards false reporting which in the absence of any effective checking, demoralises the honest workers and encourages the boosters who succeed in earning a prize or a good character roll entry or good-will of the bosses. I came across a case in which a district in a certain State was awarded a shield for the largest area put under Japanese method of paddy cultivation. Next year when the programme was put on a wider front, the same district fixed up a target which was less than half the achievement of the previous year for which it was awarded the shield. When asked to explain, the explanation was that the work was being done on more systematic lines, and therefore, the target fixed was less than the achievement of the last year.

(*xx*) There has developed mostly one-way channel of working between the higher officers and the people. Orders flow from the top to bottom without regard for the experiences of the people or the workers at the spot. A few experiences that are gathered by touring officers are the only experiences that the higher officers get. Even some of these experiences gathered on tours are hearsay experiences narrated to please the officers. Most of the workers do not like to tell the correct position for fear of incurring displeasure.

(*xxi*) Promises made regarding supplies are many a time not fulfilled resulting in dislocation of the work of the farmers and giving rise to lack of confidence of the people in the local workers. In one district, green manure seed scheduled to reach in the month of May reached by the middle of August, when the time for sowing it had already passed. The district officers for fear of the audit and the higher bosses issued orders to the blocks for immediate distribution of this seed even though it could not be sown by the farmers. These orders from the district to the blocks and in turn from the blocks to the village level workers resulted in a forced distribution of the seed. In some cases when the entire seed could not be distributed, the cost of the undistributed quantity was realised from the pay of the village level workers. The village level workers in turn, tried to force the seed upon the people by linking it with some other supplies. It would be seen that a little carelessness on the part of somebody resulted in the demoralisation of the staff at all levels and loss to the farmers. The village level workers also suffered a monetary loss by being forced to pay the cost of the undistributed seed and ultimately their families suffered.

(*xxii*) A good number of subordinates do not work sincerely but behave in a way that they seem to work a great deal. They generally try to develop 4 to 5 show-pieces for the visitors or higher officers and bank upon them throughout. Such show-pieces are prepared in every season and are shown alternately to visitors coming periodically. Subordinates of these types are liked by most of the bosses because their show-pieces serve as very good examples of the type of work done by the staff and they have no time to go to other places. As the immediate impression of the bosses visiting the block is good, everything goes on well and in that atmosphere, the idea of developing a few show-pieces gains ground and gets precedence over other methods of working.

There is no harm in visiting such show-pieces as they would tell about the best which the workers could bring about but it should also be the policy to see a few villages at random so that one is able to see the general conditions. Best is already the best, but what is more necessary is to raise the average and make it better.

(*xxiii*) There is an absence of systematic evaluation of pro-grammes. Whatever evaluation is done, is done on the basis of progress reports or the views expressed or information given by the immediate subordinates. This evaluation is generally not based on what the lower ladder of workers or people themselves feel about the programme. Such an evaluation does not in the majority of the cases give a real picture as it is not based upon the experiences of those who actually handle the programme or are affected by the programme.

(*xxiv*) Jeeps given to the block development officers are a constant source of trouble. There are regular complaints about their use both by the extension staff and the people's representatives. It is contended that the block development officers keep those jeeps as if it is their private property and do not allow their use for the furtherance of the programmes in general. The dis-trict level departmental and revenue officers do not possess any official vehicle. They feel jealous of the block development offi-cer who is junior to them. This jealousy results in a perpetual misunderstanding and bickerings.

(*xxv*) There is hardly any sense of loyalty and respect among the staff for their seniors. This is mostly due to the wrong approach of the seniors themselves.

(*xxvi*) The meetings held to take decisions are conducted in a true democratic spirit. On the contrary views of superior offi-cers are imposed without any consideration for what the workers actually feel about their views. The composition of these meetings is generally very heterogeneous. Some participants have actually no touch with the matters at issue. They generally have some vague ideas, but when discussion is held they seem to pose that they have a detailed idea of the subject. These members, if they happen to be senior in status or rank become the dominating figures. Such meetings can serve best as training grounds for the heterogeneous element without any reciprocal gain for the other participants. This reduces the seriousness of these meetings.

(*xxvii*) Staff meetings which are considered to be a co-ordinating forum to pool field experience, and chalking out a programme with common agreement, do not serve this purpose if the senior members dominate in them. If the chairman is imbued with the extension philosophy, he tries to conduct such meetings in an atmosphere of freedom where mutual discussions take place to the advantage of one and all and full advantage is taken of the experiences of the field workers. The credit lies when everybody present in the meeting has a feeling of equal partnership and responsibility for all the decisions taken in the meeting. This is necessary and this is the test of the success of a meeting.

Many workers apparently agree to the decisions taken but retain sufficient mental reservations which seal the fate of programmes. Mental reservations should not be allowed to be developed, and if they are already there, workers should be encouraged to come out with them.

(*xxviii*) There is lack of co-ordination in programmes. It is often forgotten that almost all problems require a co-ordinated and joint action and a team approach to solve them. Feeling of departmentalism is often responsible for lack of co-ordination and it can be dispelled only through indirect educative process, and proper approach to problems.

A good many departments of government take a very narrow view of things. The officers manning them hold a particular view about a matter when they are on a particular post. Their views are often seen changing drastically after they are transferred to some other post and work there for some time. This is because their views are based on whatever insufficient study or knowledge of the subject they possess or on the advice tendered by the immediate subordinates who try to circle round them without giving them any opportunity to think and study things independently. As this advice is difficult to be ignored on account of the resultant administrative indifference or non-co-operation on the part of the subordinates, indifferent or even wrong decisions are taken on many vital matters which require broad and co-ordinated thinking.

Sometimes inapt decisions are taken on account of the insistence of the presiding officer who happens to be a senior person in rank or status. Such decisions if the officers of the concerned departments do not like them are afterwards secretly sabotaged or made ineffective in good many cases.

The evil of departmentalism is one of the chief factors responsible for failures of several governmental or privately sponsored programmes. Many departments think that their duty or function is only to go so far and no further. Such rigidness results in lack of co-ordination. There is hardly any programme which does not need the co-operation of one or two departments to make it a complete success. Programmes cannot be taken up successfully, and in a comprehensive manner if all the departments concerned do not co-ordinate. The following examples would explain this point better:

a. *Control of malaria* :

Malaria becomes a very serious menace during September and October in several parts of the country. This period is very vital to *Rabi* seed-bed preparation, but about 30 to 40 per cent of the people of such areas become victim of this disease and in consequence the agricultural operations suffer badly. If the workers of the agriculture department feel that control of malaria is not their job, it would be quite wrong to think so, as it directly affects their programme by reducing the effective manpower available for agricultural purposes. To succeed in agricultural work during this period, it is necessary for the agricultural staff to co-ordinate properly with the public health department and see that proper control measures are carried out for prevention and eradication of malaria from the villages. It does not mean that they have to run this programme themselves, but it does mean that they have to be alive to this problem and co-ordinate with the public health officials in preventing and eradicating malaria by providing all necessary help. This equally applies to the public health department.

b. *Construction of culverts and bridges on roads*:

Culverts and bridges on roads are necessary to allow surplus water to pass. If they are constructed in such a way as to ensure that the surplus water that passes through them does not carry with it any eroded soil, their construction would help soil and water conservation programme also. If the two departments co-ordinate their programmes properly, far-reaching results would be achieved in preserving the fertile soil of watersheds which otherwise would be washed away due to erosion.

c. *Pisciculture and irrigation dams*:

There is a great need of close co-ordination and co-operation between the fisheries and irrigation departments in respect of pisciculture in large irrigation dams being constructed by the irrigation department. These dams can be utilised for irrigation purposes as well as for pisciculture to produce valuable food for the people.

Once the irrigation department of a certain State requested the animal husbandry department of the same State to develop pisciculture in one of the important dams constructed by them. The animal husbandry department replied that it would first survey the project before committing anything. The survey took about a year. After the survey, the animal husbandry department agreed to take up the work but wrote to the irrigation department that it should get at least 2/3rd of the receipts accruing from the sale of fish. The irrigation department did not agree to this demand and offered a share of 33% of the receipts only. Correspondence on this aspect continued for a year without the matter being settled. Both the departments in this case belonged to the same government and receipt of any would have been the receipt of the same government, but still the correspondence continued and as the result the work of pisciculture in this important dam was delayed by about two years resulting in a loss of about 20,000 tons of fish. Who lost this production?—not the persons incharge of the programme in the departments but the people. Such instances of departmentalism result in a great loss to the government or the organisation and sooner they are checked, the better it would be for the good of the government and the people. All such instances should be checked with a strong hand.

d. *Construction of a multipurpose building in each Gram Sabha:*

Different departments are constructing different kinds of buildings at the *Panchayat* level. *Panchayat Raj* department is constructing *Panchayatghars*. *Zila Parishads* are constructing buildings for schools. Co-operative department is constructing godowns and an office for service co-operatives. Community development department is constructing community centres at several places. If all the departments construct their buildings separately, not only more land will be required, but also considerably more money. *Panchayatghars* are only used occasionally and they could be easily used for the running of primary or secondary schools. A hall provided for in the building for holding meetings could also be used as community or information centre.

Besides the economy in the buildings, all the activities in the village would be concentrated at one place. This would also save considerable repairs and maintenance charges. The services of school boys, teachers and the community as a whole could be utilised for the maintenance of the building as well as the compound.

Consolidation department could be persuaded to allocate land for construction of such multipurpose buildings in each village at some central place.

The above proposal requires a co-ordinated approach on the part of the *Panchayat Raj,* community department, co-operative, education and consolidation departments and the *Zila Parishads*.

e. Soil conservation:

The main responsibility of soil conservation as a subject in many States is of the agriculture department, but several departments are concerned with this work as given below:

Forest Department:	Responsible for aforestation, plantation and checking erosion.
Animal Husbandry Department:	Controlled grazing is an important item of soil conservation. Development of proper pastures with controlled grazing is the responsibility of this department.
Irrigation Department:	Responsible for constructing dams, reservoirs, raising villages against floods, draining water-logged areas, constructing irrigation channels, etc.
Public Works Department:	Responsible for making roads, constructing culverts and bridges which allow excess water to pass.
Consolidation Department:	Responsible for Mend Bundi operations, layout of roads and channels during consolidation.
Agriculture Department:	Responsible for undertaking soil conservation measures in cultivated lands and also in others on watershed basis, changing agricultural practices to check erosion.
Community Development Department:	Responsible for helping the agriculture department in properly educating the farmers through its block agency for adoption of soil conservation programmes.

(*xxix*) There is no team work and sincere co-operation in programmes. Real co-operation is there only when individuals are willing to go well beyond their line of action in order to help one another.

Co-operation is generally of two types:

a. Horizontal, and

b. Vertical

Horizontal co-operation includes all acts of the worker outside the line of his duty with a view to making things easier for the co-worker.

Vertical co-operation includes all acts of co-operation with the immediate superior, higher superiors and with his juniors.

Co-operation has to be in both the directions, *i.e.*, horizontal as well as vertical. It becomes lop-sided if greater emphasis is placed on either of them.

Field workers could be broadly classified into four types on the basis of co-operation given by them:

a. Good in horizontal co-operation.

b. Good in vertical co-operation.

c. Good in both horizontal and vertical co-operation.

d. Poor in both types of co-operation.

Within these four broad categories all sorts of combinations are found depending upon the nature and personality of the individuals. The best workers are those who belong to the (c) category.

A larger number of field workers, however, belong to category (b). This category of co-operation can be divided into two: (i) Upward co-operation and (ii) downward co-operation. Even in category (b) most workers belong to (b) (i) vertical upward category. They go out to co-operate with and please their superiors at any cost and try to find fault with their juniors. The workers who belong to category (b) (ii) vertical downward co-operation generally possess the knack of winning co-operation from their subordinates but do not like to take orders from their superiors. Such a person develops kingdom of his own in which subordinates remain intensely loyal to him and follow his deeds and even sometimes display antagonism towards his superiors at his instance.

(xxx)   A tendency to form water-tight compartments in executing programmes of their respective departments is developing in the workers. This is very harmful to the interest of programmes. One regional officer in a certain State once wrote in his monthly demi-official letter to the Development Commissioner of that State about the attitude of the workers of a particular department as below:

"News came that this year where there was a deficiency of moisture, there appeared a hard-skinned insect which ate the germinating plumule as soon as it emerged above ground and turned green. The ordinary DDT did not have any effect on this insect. On the advice of my Commissioner, I wrote to the headquarters of the concerned organisation who immediately sent one of his officers to my region. This officer along with his junior assistant saw me and told me that it was possible to control the insect, and that the control measures were to be carried out free of cost. If necessary a squad could also be sent to control it. When I asked him as to what he had done in this matter till then, he said: 'I have not received any report of the attack'. It appeared as if he had no responsibility for periodically contacting the field workers and collecting the news concerning his programmes. He waited for others to inform him. My idea is not to blame any particular person, but to point out the hollowness of the approach of the official machinery, which does not see the fire raging around without a formal report being made to it and if it does see it, it does not feel any pain about the loss suffered by the farmers, because it always has sufficient excuse to escape the responsibility with the help of defective departmental rules and procedures. They move about only when some farmer or official comes to their doors, agrees to abide by all the departmental rules and conditions and deposits money in advance. If there is going to be any real use of the service provided to the farmers, by government, the workers manning such services should always remain alert, move about and observe things themselves otherwise they can never render timely servic to save anything."

This case history is typical of the attitude of a good number of workers. Such an attitude always keeps the workers at a distance from the people whom they are meant to serve.

(*xxxi*) Most of the decisions are taken by the seniors without consulting the team workers which may consist of the workers of the same department or several departments. Vertical decisions seldom carry conviction except that they are executed mechanically. Horizontal decisions, however, taken in a democratic way by a team presided over by the boss carry conviction. Every member of the team feels that he is a partner in the decision and, therefore, he works with conviction behind it. If this feeling is not ensured, the chances are that the decisions taken would not have unanimous backing or faith of the workers in them and would not be whole-heartedly implemented.

(*xxxii*) A pernicious tendency is that in meetings no departmental worker feels himself competent to take independent decisions. They generally remain non-committal and as the result all decisions taken at horizontal level are generally referred again to the higher officers of the concerned departments for approval. This leads to a lot of delay.

(*xxxiii*) There is usually a long circuit of correspondence in most of the offices. The letters before they are replied to, pass through several hands—about a dozen sometimes right from receipt to despatch. If the letter is replied to with some query or objection, it has again to pass through two sets of hands—once in the office where the letter originated and a second time in the office which is supposed to send the final reply. The number of hands through which a letter passes before a reply, varies from office to office and office to officer. When delay occurs as the result of unnecessary formalities, the objectives with which the letters are written are in most cases not fulfilled. Time is a major factor in the execution of programmes and if it is lost, success almost becomes remote.

(*xxxiv*) Rules and regulations get undue priority. Although one has to work within their framework, yet if they are observed just formally, business cannot be transacted expeditiously and efficiently. Most of the troubles in extension are due to rigid obedience to rules and regulations without taking into consideration the local factors. These rules need to be completely overhauled to meet the present-day requirements of speed with which the programme is expected to be executed. Fear of punishment for even small infringement of rules and regulations, without regard to the requirement of the situation is one of the main factors demoralising the official machinery. It drains out all initiative from the workers and creates a "penny-wise and pound-foolish" attitude in them. Those who are the custodians of rules and regulations, guard them as jealous treasure with great rigidity. Their minds get too much conditioned by formal technicalities of procedure with the result that they do not yield to actual considerations for doing quick work or real justice. Of course, rules have to be observed but not at the cost of programmes and facility for work.

(*xxxv*) Demonstrations which are the basis of successful extension of agricultural programmes are neglected because of pressure of far too large a number of programmes on the village level workers and the block development officers. They are laid out in most cases, but they are seldom followed to the finish. The result is that labour and money spent on their lay-out is more or less wasted.

(*xxxvi*) Administration is becoming top-heavy. There are 8 to 11 subject-matter specialists at the block headquarters, besides the block development officer. The number of these subject-matter specialists is thus almost the same as the number of village level workers. Each of these specialists expects to get his work done by the village level workers. The result is that the village level worker does not know whom to obey and when. Some subject-matter specialist or the block development officer is always there in his circle at least for 20 to 25 days in a month for each is required to make 12 to 15 night halts during a month. When should he work? Every person wants that he should dance in attendance on him. As the subject-matter specialists do not get the facility of any peon or the use of jeep for transportation of their kits, they move without any kits of their own. The village level worker has, therefore, to arrange for their boarding and lodging. This is demoralising to the village level workers. Similar is the fate of block development officers whose blocks are visited during the month by more than half a dozen district and regional officers who report on his work besides the outside visitors. The staff thus remains busy for a pretty long time during the month in taking round seniors and visitors and looking after their comforts.

On account of lack of facilities for transport of kits and lodging, night halts are not commonly made in a good number of cases. The workers go in the morning and return late in the night and note it down as night halt. When a large number of workers in the block behave this way nobody in the block is in a position to check the wrong because most of them are a party to it.

These are unpalatable truths not squarely faced by those who count. This leads to complete suppression of facts and demoralisation of workers. The proper thing is to admit the difficulties of the workers by putting oneself in their position.

A very interesting description of defects that ensued due to expansion of the community development programme has been given by the report of the Community Development Evaluation Mission in India organised at the request from the Government of India, by the United Nations Technical Assistance Administration. It would be interesting to quote them here:

Results of Forcing the Pace

The pace of programme planning and of extending programmes in additional areas was suddenly forced by the urgent national need for speeding up agricultural production, especially of food, and by the general political and social situation, demanding a nation-wide planned approach to community development and no longer a limited experimental project approach.

The result of this expansion was the creation of an army of officials to plan and execute community development in all the States and at the Centre. These officials had to be drawn from a number of existing technical and administrative departments.

with no experience of the new multi-purpose community development approach to village problems. Furthermore, the great majority had no clear concept, and some had none at all, of what community development was about, and, above all, that community development was aiming at helping the villagers to shake off the bonds of their poverty and to take a share in creating a new future for themselves and their family and their village.

The village level worker and his supporting advisers

In these circumstances, it was probably right to concentrate on the village level worker. He was the man among the community development officials who was destined to be in close and constant touch with village people. The ultimate execution of plans, formed at the state and national level, rested in his inexperienced hands. At first his training was, in the exigencies of the situation, brief and inadequate, but it was always hoped that his rural background—for the early recruitment gave preference to young men who came from village homes, would make him sympathetic with farming families and able to understand the nature and complexity of their problems.

He had, however, neither enough technical knowledge to give adequate help, nor a wide enough general education to be able to see the inter-relatedness of bad farming methods, malnutrition and disease, illiteracy, and the bondage of debt. For the technical side of his job, he, therefore, depended on the extension advisers at the block level who formed the next echelon in the community development hierarchy above him. These, in turn, needed supervising on the technical side and organising on the administrative side in order that the multipurpose approach, as typified by the village level worker, might be maintained. We have seen, however, that at least 75% of his time was necessarily devoted to agriculture, and while that was inadequate, the other aspects of his work were also handled inadequately.

Results of rapid expansion of staff

There were two almost inevitable results from this rapid expansion of staff in community development programmes:

1. It became easier to transmit a community development programme from the top downwards in the form of a nation-wide, or at least statewide, series of common targets and common methods, of achieving those targets. Many of these targets were of universal application and importance. Many were applicable in certain areas and wide of the mark in other areas. As a result of the uniformity in community development programmes it was easier to pin down achievements to the achievement of visible targets, whether in agriculture or village improvement. The emphasis was on instruction about methods and the calculation of necessary finances, including labour contributions from the villagers, in order to attain these achievemets; and

2. The other result of the rapid expansion of programmes and staff, equally inevitable as the former, was that the original aim of stimulating and drawing out the village people's initiative and whole-hearted co-operation came a bad second to the apparent necessity to the production of more visible and concrete results. There was neither time, nor was it the most direct method, to wait for villagers to make their own plans, work out how to execute them, ask for advice, and then proceed to calculate how much financial help they needed. Hence, the recent changeover in some blocks which had completed their five or six years' programme from stage I to stage II, with the consequent decrease in block funds available, has found the villagers on the whole unprepared to take up full responsibility for programmes, either in terms of planning or financing.

Distance between staff and village conditions

It seems to be a law of human relationships that, as staff of a service department grows, involving more and more supervision by a constantly growing number of supervisors, the whole staff grows increasingly further away from the grass-roots level of the conditions which must be improved.

The pertinence of this law is clearly demonstrated in the Indian community development programme. The rapid growth of the community development staff has meant that they have moved increasingly further away from the original impetus and clarity of vision of the former small circle of community development workers. Hence, there has arisen a need for a "philosophy of community development" couched in general terms, which sometimes seem remote from village realities. There has also arisen a necessity for orientation courses to acquaint the staff, already on the job, with this general philosophy.

Need for radical re-thinking by the staff

The community development staff at present, however, largely think in terms of programmes dictated or indicated on a state or national level and of how to spend the allocations of money. They have to do a radical re-thinking of their job, a *volte-face*, in fact, if they are to put themselves in the place of village people who look at these programmes from an internal and not an external point of view. The villagers think of improvements in terms of "my family, my farm, my village." When villagers talk, they often refer to a general village situation and sometimes to the block, but seldom if ever, to the over-all concept of community development.

Lines of communication

As regards the lines of communication between the top level and the village level, they exist administratively, in the ordered hierachy of official responsibility for action, worked out in detail —in far too great detail—at every level. There may however, be some lack of understanding among the top level officials about how to transmit their new thinking about community development to all the officials below them, or the very size of the official community development machine may make this particular kind of communication difficult; at any rate, the existing lines of communication seem to be blocked. Many, perhaps the majority of the community development officials, are on the whole, out of touch with village expectations. Officials regard their function as being mainly to instruct and to 'organise', and seldom to sit patiently and listen until the slowly-formulated realistic thoughts of the villagers come to the surface. This patience and capacity for listening to villagers is brilliantly demonstrated by some of the very top level officials. But while they sit quietly and wait for the villagers to speak, a flock of minor officials buzz around, wanting to demonstrate their acti-vities, to push plans and figures under the eyes of the high official and prove that they have been 'on the job'.

The Mission found several examples of the ways in which the lines of communication from the top downwards through all the echelons of community development officials are blocked. Officials in the lower ranks still talk about the 'felt-needs' of the villagers and the peculiarity of the 'rural mind'. Top-level com-munity development officials have long since discarded this ter-minology, if indeed they ever used it, for they are refreshingly free of catchwords and blanket terms which confuse and disguise the real issues. One must, therefore, wonder why handbooks, texts and training syllabuses on various aspects of community development still contain all these outdated catchwords. In many training centres they are certainly faithfully taught and dutifully learned, with strange results.

Until these lines of communications are opened up, and the free flow of ideas can be assured from the very top level down through all the ranks of officials, and from the village level up through the ranks of officials, the whole community develop-ment programmes cannot be, in the words of the latest com-munity development report, 'revitalised'. The vitality is there at the very top level, and to an increasing extent in the villages themselves. But some kind of drastic change involving a more alert and open mind, and a real desire to get alongside village people, has to take place among the community development officials at every level above the village level worker, and includ-ing, sometimes, the village level worker himself.

(7) *Remedies*

The above defects, howsoever unpalatable they may appear to us, are real facts. They should be taken note of and con-stant efforts made to remedy them. Those who are responsible for manning the official machinery, at whatever level and posi-tion they may be, cannot ignore these defects and complications and allow them to continue. Man always learns through mis-takes and if this is kept in view every mistake committed and subsequently remedied and not repeated later will make us better and more experienced in life to assume greater and greater responsibilities for undertaking even complicated programmes. Concrete steps that are recommended to remove these defects and complications are:

a. *Proper selection of personnel*: Selection of proper personnel is the key to the success of all programmes. It should, therefore, be done with utmost care and integrity of purpose. Those persons or authorities who meddle with proper selection of the personnel are the greatest enemies of the programme and the people.

b. *Training of the selected personnel*: Not only lower ladder of workers should be trained but also higher level of workers. Often it is thought that training of higher ladder of workers is not necessary. This is a very erroneous notion. Programmes, however simple they may appear, need proper methodology and technique to be followed for their successful implementation. Hence the necessity of training.

Meyer (1956) in one of his lectures to a Cornell University seminar in U.S.A. pointed out that Indian workers generally lack:

(*i*) Courage and toughness;
(*ii*) Intellectual honesty;
(*iii*) Systematibility;
(*iv*) Thoroughness; and
(*v*) Self-reliance.

It is difficult to controvert what he has said. It is, therefore, advisable if special stress were laid on these defects in our training programmes.

c. *Periodical assessment of the reactions of the workers and taking action in respect of them*: Periodical assessment of the reactions of the workers by the seniors and taking action in respect of them is very necessary to build up confidence in the juniors. Their reactions should be collected both formally and informally and taken advantage of, to remove the difficulties of the workers and to suitably modify the programme. Although these reactions can be very effectively collected formally at the staff meetings, it would be better to have informal meetings where the workers would speak more freely. Dube[10] (1958) working in Deoband Community Development Block of Saharanpur district in Uttar Pradesh studied the reactions of 17 village level workers. Their reactions are summarised below as a typical example of what the village level workers thought of the community development programme at that time.

(i) *Staff meetings*

Eleven village level workers out of 17 said that they had practically no freedom of expression in the staff meetings. The remaining 6 said that they could express themselves quite freely. Many of those who said that they could express themselves freely, doubted about its effectiveness.

These meetings have very heavy agenda. Programmes are received in the form of orders from above and they are reported to have been passed on to them for execution without ascertaining their views.

(ii) *Targets*

Eleven village level workers out of 17 said that they had to carry out the orders and wishes of their officers and had to achieve targets fixed by those at the top.

In reply as to what the job of village level workers was, 14 village level workers out of 17 said that their job was to achieve targets fixed at the top. One said that his job was to discover felt-needs of the people and on their basis to help in the determination of community development programme targets. Another said that his job was to convey the demands of the village people to higher government officials. The remaining one said that his job was both to discover felt-needs with a view to fixing targets and to achieve targets fixed by the higher projects officials.

[10] Dube, S. C. (1958)—India's changing villages—Human factors in Community Development. **Printed by Routledge and Kegan Paul Ltd.,** London.

Sixteen village level workers out of 17 said that they could not contribute effectively to the formulation of programme targets. They had learnt to accept targets fixed by higher officers. There was practically no sphere in which they could act on their own initiative for they needed permissions, sanctions or orders for doing nearly everything.

Most of them said that they could not contribute much to overall programme planning because the project was under pressure from above to undertake specific lines of action decided at the State level.

(iii) *Training*

Some common reactions about the training were:

(*a*) Great emphasis was laid in the training centres on the grass-root planning and that plans should grow up from the village people but in reality they found that the plan invariably came from the top and had to be carried down to the village people.

(*b*) Although it was emphasised at the training centres that in working out community development programmes, traditional bureaucratic methods would not be followed, but the actual field experience was otherwise.

(*c*) Timely support, supplies and co-ordinated efforts promised to them in the course of their training were seldom available.

(iv) *Supplies*

Most of the village level workers complained about frequent delays in supplies grant of funds, bad quality of supplies and charging of prices higher than the prevalent market prices. They felt that such things greatly affected their reputation and good-will among the people.

The block staff, they said, had very little control over the quality and even the quantity of materials supplied by departmental agency. It was a vicious circle. When the officers are disappointed by their superior officers they had to disappoint those who were working under them. It was not always wise or practical to protect against the decisions of the State headquarters.

(v) *Building up prestige*

Most of them said when dignitaries and important guests visited their villagers, they were relegated to a back position and were utilised for running errands instead of being accorded a place of some respect or honour. Officers rebuked them in public and the result their prestige suffered. There is no effort to build up their prestige in the villages. Two of them said that flattering their superiors and going out of their way to please them had become one of their most important duties.

(vi) *Co-operation*

There is no co-operation from the *Lekhpal,* Patrol, tubewell operator or the cane supervisor. They cannot approach them direct but only through their officers, namely tahsildar, ziledar, overseer or assistant cane development officer respectively.

(vii) *Financial regulations*

Financial regulations are very rigid. Some of the project programmes are inflexible. A good many reactions of the extension workers about their difficulties and programmes are published in several Indian papers like *Gram Sevak,* "Extension", *Kurukshetra, etc.* These reactions should be carefully studied and taken advantage of. Some common difficulties and reactions given out by the workers and published in these papers are described below without giving their names:

(*i*) There are eight assistant development officers in each block who sleep happily at the Block headquarters. Their work is only to collect and compile instructions received from higher officers, on the previous day of the staff meeting and to pass them on to the village level workers for necessary action. They feel that their responsibility is over as soon as they read out these circulars of the higher officers before the village level workers.

(This example shows what a village level worker feels about the assistant development officers. It appears that in this particular block the assistant development officers did not provide any guidance to the village level workers).

(*ii*) All assistant development officers do not attend the staff meetings. If there is any problem for the absentee assistant development officer to solve, it remains unattended to. Workers are assured that it would be answered when the assistant development officer would be there. As most of the agricultural programmes are seasonal, the problem remains generally unsolved.

(*iii*) Impractical orders are issued at the staff meetings. If any village level worker tries to discuss the merits of the order, he is rebuffed. He, therefore, sits quiet.

(*iv*) There is the difficulty of housing in the villages. If any particular person gives his house, he tries to take undue advantage from the worker. As the result of this, the workers are identified with parties.

(*v*) The equipment that is given to the workers is damaged because of lack of space for its storage. They are expected to keep them in their houses. Sometimes there are poisonous medicines in the kit. They are always apprehensive lest their children should eat them.

(*vi*) As the assistant development officers and block development officers do not get travelling and daily allowances for journeys within five miles radius they avoid visiting these villages.

(*vii*) One or the other subject-matter specialist whose number has greatly increased is always in the village level worker's circle. This greatly dislocates the work.

Studies of the above nature are necessary to be undertaken by all senior officers at different levels. Such informal studies followed by appropriate action really serve as an excellent guide to improve and modify the programmes and bring about a change in the attitude of the workers and build up confidence in them.

(d) *Staff meetings*

The staff meetings are a forum to meet all junior workers, colleagues and seniors, to discuss programmes, review progress, exchanges views, resolve difficulties, arrange and check supplies and services and finalise targets for the next period.

Senior officers must attend staff meetings as they provide the best opportunity to come face to face with the workers in the field.

Staff meetings should always be conducted in a way that the workers feel that all decisions taken in them are taken in consultation with them and they are a party to them. Normally decisions taken at the staff meetings should never be nullified or cancelled without consulting the members again.

All members in the staff meeting, whether senior or junior, should have a free say. The seniors should not feel prejudiced against the juniors, if the latter try to give a frank opinion. In fact, seniors should welcome frank talks and encourage them. They should always utilise the staff meetings for giving guidance and even training in certain programmes. Guidance and training given at the spot are much more effective and useful than that given through correspondence.

(e) *Seminars*

Staff meetings are meetings of the workers of the same project or those engaged in the same work in a given area. Seminars, on the other hand, are meetings of workers working in different areas representing different aspects of a programme. Seminars, thus, help to bring together personnel from a wider area with wider interests. They provide a very good forum for exchange of views and experiences and for greater acquisition of knowledge. By coming into contact with one another, workers develop a healthy rivalry. Seminars of workers of similar interests working at different places should, therefore, be a regular feature of any extension programme.

(f) *Study tours*

Nothing convinces a person more than what he sees himself. Study tours of successful projects elsewhere provide this opportunity. They should, therefore, be encouraged as much as possible as a medium for changing the outlook of workers and the people and creating a spirit of healthy jealousy and rivalry in programmes.

Study tours should not only be confined to adult males but also to women, girls and youths. The latter, especially women, play a great part in extension of agricultural and community development programmes, and therefore, a change in their outlook can help a great deal in moulding the countryside.

(g) *Decentralisation of power*

Concentration of power at the top or in a few individuals is very detrimental to the extension of programmes in the long run. Care is to be taken to ensure that there is maximum decentralisation of power. Work should be carried out more by putting reliance on and having confidence in workers than through sanctions and fiats.

Many a time enthusiastic workers take initiative and carry out programmes with success but in doing so commit several procedural irregularities. It is a wrong policy to punish workers for such irregularities. If the motive in committing an irregularity is to promote a programme, it should always be regularised. Punishing workers for procedural irregularities committed in good faith, demoralises them resulting in lack of initiative and enthusiasm. What is necessary, is arousing the best in them. Once initiative and enthusiasm are lost, the workers do as much as the rules safely permit and not beyond that. They either blame the programme or the rules for lack of progress.

There should always be a tendency on the part of the official machinery to decentralise power in order to share it with the workers and the people helping them to manage their own affairs. Whatever work people can do themselves after proper training and learning, they should be encouraged to do so. The official machinery should in no case try to assume responsibility of such programmes upon itself. It should be the concerted endeavour of this machinery to train people and equip them to do things themselves.

(h) *Setting personal examples by the seniors*

There is no greater force for building up the juniors than the personal examples set by the seniors in respect of honesty, integrity of purpose, impartiality and sense of urgency. Seniors have, therefore, a great responsibility, for juniors generally imitate them.

6

Seniors have to behave with their juniors in such a way as to assure indirectly that their careers are safe in their hands and whatever they do, is in their larger interests, and in the interest of the State and the programme. Such a feeling in the juniors is a valuable asset of the seniors and those who help to create such a feeling in them succeed most with them.

Seniors by and large should be able to do themselves all what they hope to get done from the juniors. Unless they possess this quality, they are never able to remove the practical difficulties of the juniors. Such difficulties can possibly be removed only when the seniors have experience of the job.

The best guiding point for the seniors for behaving with their juniors is that they should behave with them just in the same way as they would like their own seniors to behave with them. If this golden rule is followed, there would never be any misbehaviour on the part of the seniors towards their juniors.

Specially when the responsibility for execution of programmes is passing at the block and district levels to the people themselves, the official machinery specially the senior officers amongst it have a major role to play in training and guiding not only their juniors, but also the representatives of the people themselves.

Love for inner democratisation, feeling of equal partnership in the formulation and execution of programmes amongst all level of workers, team spirit, sense of urgency about the programme and people's welfare, respect for juniors and the people, tendency to delegate power to the people and making them manage their own affairs are some of the important qualities besides others which the seniors should try to possess themselves and help to develop in their juniors. This is only possible through constant persuasion and pressure by silently and persistently changing their attitude through a long term educational, training and supervisory programme. Unless this is ensured the community development programmes would always tend to show the defects and complications as pointed out in this chapter without making a permanent mark on the people.

The greatest thing in the community development programmes is constantly to enthuse workers and the people. Things come to be taken as a routine after some time and, therefore, it is necessary to infuse a new spirit both in the workers and the people by trusting them, reposing confidence in them, encouraging and giving responsibility to them, providing incentives and finally by commending impartially all those who do good work.

(i) *Define and keep to objectives*

Defining the objective in all perspective is very necessary right from the very start of a programme. After the objective has been defined, one has to adhere to the aim of achieving the objective and not be led astray by anything else less vital.

Continuity in thinking and working with a well defined objective, adopting proper means is essential for success. A tendency is developing among workers to initiate a programme or start a drive, carry it half way and change or replace it suddenly with another programme or drive. Nothing is more prejudicial to the cause of extension than such a tendency. Come what may, a programme once started with some well defined objective, should be carried through to the finish.

(j) *Use of correct means to achieve the desired ends*

Means employed affect the ends and therefore, good ends can be achieved only through proper means. As against this, the tendency to achieve ends anyhow, is wrong. This tendency is more among untrained workers than in workers trained in extension philosophy. It may lead to temporary success, but ultimately it proves harmful and recoils badly on the worker himself. The field workers should therefore, always adopt the right means to achieve their ends.

A case history illustrating the point may be of interest here.

In March 1958, a district level officer in a certain State found that out of the total amount of loan allotted in a particular block for distribution of fertilizers, Rs. 2,710 had not yet been utilised. The block development officer proposed to surrender this amount, but the district level officer insisted on its being utilised. On seeing the insistence of the district level officer, the block development officer called his extension officer (agriculture) and threatened to take serious action against him if the amount was not utilised. He in turn collected the village level workers and threatened them. The village level workers on account of the threat prepared false applications for the loan in the names of certain genuine cultivators. These applications were handed over to the seedstore incharge, who was asked to prepare a bill for the fertilizer supplied. It was promised that the fertilizer would be lifted later on. A bill was prepared for the transaction by the supervisor and the amount paid to the agriculture department without distribution of any fertilizer. Thus the total amount of fertilizer loan was utilised. No subsequent steps were taken to dispose off the fertilizer to the cultivators in whose names the applications were prepared. The then block development officer resigned in May-June 1958 and the extension officer (social education) took over the charge from him. This man was also transferred in September 1958 to another block in the same district. A new block development officer from another district took his place. After some time of his joining, the extension officer (agriculture) explained to him the case, but in a different form. He desired the block development officer to coax the village level workers to get the fertilizer lifted by the cultivators. The block development officer called the village level workers and told them to get the fertilizer lying at the seedstore lifted by the cultivators. Of the 48 cultivators concerned, 21 lifted the fertilizer on persuasion of the village level workers, but 27 cultivators complained to the sub-divisional officer through an application that they never applied for the loan and that they are being harassed by the village level workers, extension officers and the block development officer to forcibly lift the fertilizer. The sub-divisional officer passed on the application to the block development officer for enquiry. The block development officer personally met the villagers and on enquiry found that the fertilizer was never taken by them. The loan papers were also found lying in his office and were not sent to the revenue department for realisation. Immediately he got the papers completed and sent them to the revenue department for realisation. The fertilizer lying at the seedstore was also sold on cash. The receipts from the sale of fertilizer were deposited as payment towards Taqavi in the names of the same cultivators. The entire loan amount was thus deposited in the treasury except the interest. That block development officer was also subsequently transferred. The account of the loan was not adjusted till 1962. The cultivators who complained to the sub-divisional officer did not take any fertilizer next year also either in cash or kind for the fear that they might be again entangled in some compli- cations by the block staff.

The loan allotted for distribution of fertilizers was, thus dis- bursed during the year in question in full, without distribution of the corresponding quantities of fertilizers. The use of wrong means to achieve the end resulted in considerable hindrance to the subsequent spread of the programme of distribution of fertilizer. At least it made all the 48 cultivators and many others who came to know about it hardened in their attitude towards the block staff. They became over cautious and lost all faith in the programme and the workers. Instances of this type of using wrong means to achieve an end, do more harm than good. The greatest harm is in the direction of loss of face and prestige of the extension workers in the eyes of the people. This is a big loss—much bigger than the loss in pro- duction due to non-distribution of fertilizers.

CHAPTER IV

THE EXTENSION WORKER*

(1) *Process of Socialisation*

EVERY INDIVIDUAL has some inherent behaviour characteristics which keep on changing with his varying contacts with the social environment, education and training planned by the society according to its traditions, customs, values, habits and outlook for making new changes and adjustments. Much depends on how the individual is handled and socialised by the society right from infancy till he is put on a job to serve the society. This 'process of socialisation' consists of the interaction of the social environment begun at home by parents, neighbours, friends and others with the personality of the individual. It is helped by the institutional and non-institutional basic education and training, professional experience and guidance provided by the seniors and colleagues.

(2) *Selection of the extension worker*

There is almost no control of the employer on the socialisation process of the individual before his selection for extension work. The impact of the employer starts only after the selection.

The first thing, therefore, before starting any extension programme is selection of the extension worker. The selection is

*The term 'extension worker' in this chapter refers to all village or block level staff belonging to different agencies or departments of government and includes the staff in the community development and national extension blocks in India.

generally made on the basis of some kind of competitive practical and theoretical pre-selection tests for judging intelligence, general knowledge, professional background, attitude and temperament. These tests are followed by a *viva voce* interview. Preference is given to persons with rural background, good health and personality. All the tests or interviews are of short duration. Although they give a fairly good idea about the suitability of the candidates, they do not give any real clue to his personal qualities, skills or attitudes. These are in fact best tested during the period of pre-service training followed by on the job-training.

In cases, a regular method of selecting workers through competitive tests is not followed, on account of local pulls and considerations, the selection is not very reliable from competence and suitability points of view. The work in such cases gets a secondary consideration. Even in regular competitive selections, the tendency to interfere is of late growing very fast. This needs curbing if community development programme is to be made a success in the furtherance of the goal of the socialistic pattern of society.

In branches, where pre-service training is the rule, the selected candidates are again examined during the course of the training and also at the end of the training.

These tests are generally not very rigorous for hardly anybody is detained after the training. If this test is rigorous, it helps to spot and weed out most of the unsuitable candidates. The weeding becomes difficult when the training is once complete because of administrative difficulties and consideration of time, money and other resources spent on it. The weeding, in fact, has to be resorted to mostly in the early part of the training through rigorous work and tests and after the training only in cases where need be in the interest of the programme.

Spotting and weeding out the unsuitable workers has to be a cautious process even after they are on the job. Persons with desired qualities, attitudes and skills have always to be given preference for promotion to higher posts. It is not always necessary to condemn the unsuitable persons outright but success lies in moulding and putting them on the right path. Often indifference, lack of guidance, unnecessary punishment or bad example on the part of seniors spoils the juniors. This is to be avoided. Every attempt has to be made to give correct guidance and help the workers and only when they are incorrigible, they are to be weeded out in the interest of the programme.

The Community Development Evaluation Mission appointed under the United Nations Programme of Technical Assistance at the request of Government of India have estimated in its report, published in 1959, that as many as 25% of the persons in community development organisation at least in some States are inefficient and undesirable.[11] They have accordingly advised weeding out of these individuals in the interest of the programme along with strengthening of supervision and provision of better training. They have further said that the rate at which Community development programme expands will be very crucial to the ultimate success of the programme. "A rate of expansion that is unrealistic and too fast can only multiply existing difficulties and create illusory coverage achievements. Expansion in the form of the provision of poorly selected and inadequately trained staff for an unduly large number of villages, or of numerically inadequate staffing may greatly endanger the very foundation of the programme."

After selection starts, the real role of the employer begins. He has now to impart necessary knowledge, qualities, skills and attitudes to the persons selected through various processes of training and experiences. The success of the programme undertaken after the training depends largely on the effectiveness of these various processes of learning.

(3) *Qualities, attitude and skill of an extension worker*

The extension worker is a key person in the extension of agricultural and community development programmes. He is,

---

[11] This percentage can be easily estimated to be higher in several departments working closely with the community development programme. The pace of expansion in staff in these departments has also been very fast.

therefore, to be selected with great care and then trained properly to give him the required knowledge, skill and attitude. The qualities, attitude and skill that an ideal extension worker should have are:

a. Qualities: He should be honest, industrious, pushing, tactful, intelligent, healthy, optimistic, a good and patient listener with a wide vision. He should have a cheerful outlook and a sympathetic heart. He should be quick in appreciating the work done by the people and in giving them the due credit. He should always think, like and work with the people, identifying himself with them, sharing their joys and sorrows, hopes and doubts, enthusiasm and frustration. He should be a good planner and possess organising capacity for execution of programmes.

b. Attitude: He should have a helping, obliging, sympathetic, open, unprejudiced and friendly attitude towards the people and an objective attitude to all programmes and problems.

c. Skill: He should possess necessary skill for his job which he should be able to do and demonstrate himself.

The qualities described above should be there in all extension workers, but all of them are rarely found in any one individual. There are numerous combinations of these qualities. Each of these combinations has an equal number of different reactions on the people. These combined with the attitude and skill possessed by an individual have a great effect on the success and failure of the programmes and response of the people. A definite relationship comes to be established between the extension worker and the people on the basis of qualities, attitude and skill possessed by him and it is this relationship of comparative confidence and belief that does the trick in extension.

(4)   Development of the desired qualities, attitude and skill in the extension workers.

Many of the personal qualities and traits in individuals are inherited but there are others which are developed and fixed in the early stages of life through the process of socialisation. These matter a lot in later life and determine to what extent the individual would be helpful to society. Requisite skill and attitude can be developed through training provided the trainee has a receptive mind, intelligence and sound health. This training can be of four types, namely; (a) Pre-service training, (b) In-service training, (c) Guidance provided by the seniors and colleagues during the service, and (d) Extension worker's experience.

(a) *Pre-service training*: It prepares trainees for efficiently performing the duties of the job for which they are recruited. Its main objectives are:

(i) To impart basic knowledge, both theoretical and practical, to carry out the duties of the job;

(ii) To impart working skill both theoretical and practical, to handle the job actually;

(iii) To impart necessary attitudes to carry out the job and work with the people;

(iv) To impart training in the methods of transmission of knowledge, skills and new ideas to the individuals, groups, or communities amongst whom the trainee is expected to work after the training;

(v) To impart practical knowledge and experience about handling problems and situations commonly met with by the workers in the field;

(vi) To develop faith in the programmes and the capacity of the people to shoulder responsibility for their own welfare upon themselves;

(vii) To produce a disciplined individual with an objective bent of mind;

(viii) To prepare the worker to plan and execute various programmes and to help in thinking and analysing things for himself; and

(ix) To transform communities or the groups forming these communities in self-reliant and self-regenerating communities or groups thinking and working for themselves.

Pre-service training is a 'must' for all workers. In certain services, in which pre-service training is not given, the workers do not develop proper approach, methodology, and in many cases remain a tool in the hands of their experienced assistants.

Pre-service training prescribes a certain code of conduct for working. It does not bring about any appreciable change in his inherent qualities but it does help in changing attitudes and developing skills, enabling the worker to plan, think and analyse things for himself and tackle problems in a particular way. If one follows the code of conduct prescribed for working as an extension worker, there are certainly chances of one's success in his work even if he had originally some temperamental drawbacks. On the other hand, if he does not follow the prescribed code of conduct, he is likely to work more as a bureaucrat rather than as an extension worker.

SYLLABUS FOR THE PRE-SERVICE TRAINING

A detailed syllabus for the pre-service training should always be prepared at least two or three months in advance of the training. The syllabus should be rechecked every time a fresh batch comes for training so as to include new subjects or knowledge which may be necessary. It should be thoroughly discussed amongst the instructors, principal, representatives of the field workers and one or two representatives of the community. It should be broken up into periods for teaching having regard to the field requirements, holidays, convenience of the trainees, etc. The break up of the syllabus into periods should first be done by the individual instructors and later on discussed and finalised jointly by the entire staff in a series of staff meetings. While breaking up the syllabus into periods, care has to be taken to see that as far as possible there is not much time lag between the teaching of the theory, practical and field programmes. The lesser this gap, the better it is from the point of view of the quality of training.

Theoretical training should always go along with practical demonstrations by the instructors themselves. These should be repeated by the trainees before the instructors and then repeated at the cultivators' fields as a part of 'on the job' training under the over-all guidance of the instructors.

There is a great tendency to draw out long syllabi for the training. In the case of community development, specially for village level workers there is a great pressure from the majority of the development departments of the government to include their entire departmental programmes in the syllabi for training. The result is that there is hardly any development programme which does not find a place in the syllabus of the pre-service training of the village level workers. This entire syllabus is required to be covered between two to $2\frac{1}{2}$ years depending upon the length of pre-service training in various States.

Similar tendency to compress a large syllabus into a comparatively short period exists in the case of training of the workers belonging to different technical departments also. The report of the Community Development Evaluation Mission appointed under the United Nations Programme of Technical Assistance at the request of Government of India has made some very significant observations regarding the syllabi drawn up for training of community development workers. These are reproduced below:

"The syllabi, carefully drawn up by expert committees at New Delhi to guide and delimit the community development courses of different types look very different when seen in operation at a training centre. There they appear to demand that the staff should pack a vast amount of information into a short space of time, and as everyone knows, the easiest way to do this is by a straight lecture method. Even if the lecturer is told to leave one third of his allotted time for questions and discussions, he will not readily forego any of the points he has carefully packed into his lecture period. The result is that when he takes the last five minutes, and asks if there are any questions, the trainees' minds are numbed by the flow of information, and they only ask some of the most obvious and superficial type of questions.

"This failure to set up a lively interchange between the lecturer and the class is made worse by requiring lecturers to prepare in advance a synopsis of their lectures, and by issuing that synopsis to the students before the lecture. This is intended to obviate note taking and to promote discussion. The Mission observed that it did not by any means always have this effect. The assiduous note-taker can miss many of the lecturer's best points, but the discriminating trainee can catch hold of, and write down, points he wants to ask the lecturer about, and so maintain his part in a 'lively interchange'. Watching classes sitting with folded arms and expressions ranging from polite attention to drowsy boredom, with the synopsis (often the lecture in full) on the table in front of them, caused the Mission to wonder how much of this procedure is a waste of time, money and effort.

"One effect of these over-detailed and over-comprehensive syllabi is that, when trainees see them at the beginning of a course, they are overwhelmed by the amount of information, factual and ideological, that they must learn. They set to work to learn by the usual high school and college process of cramming and memorising. This has two main effects: they feel that they have to teach this newly acquired information to the villagers, because that is what their community development assignment requires; and they are naturally prone to give the information in package form, more or less as it has been delivered to them. They do this with their minds lulled to sleep by much learning and teaching, and anything but alert to the real problems of the villages, and to the necessity for adapting, questioning, testing all that they have heard in their training course.

"It is not difficult to see how government departments regard the provision of a detailed syllabus and its faithful implementation as a guarantee of 'value for money' in a training course. The Mission gathered enough evidence from all sides that though training courses lay down certain layers of information in the minds of the trainees, they do not stimulate a lively, alert, sensitive approach to village and rural problems.

"How can this be achieved without jettisoning the necessary basis of factual information and of accepted teaching about the aims and methods of community development?"

The Mission suggests that there are several directions in which this "educational" approach can be improved, and some of them are already being tried out by lively and enterprising principals, who, are not, however, always able to persuade their more conservative staff to adopt these methods:

(1) Members of expert committees responsible for syllabi should be in close touch with the changing village conditions. They should also visit training centres after the syllabi have been issued and impress on principals the importance of adapting the syllabus, of selecting from it and of adding to it where conditions require such changes. They should invite correspondence from principals about these adaptations;

(2) An appendix should be attached to each syllabus, containing actual problems which arise in a village context, relating to village organisation, the emergence of new leaders, the needs and attitudes of youth groups, farmers' resistances to new methods of cultivation or of obtaining credit, and so on. Such examples should be drawn from real life situations, and not invented by someone remote from village realities. The examples should be changed frequently as conditions change;

(3) The lecturer or the leader of a discussion group can either pose the problem and invite immediate discussion; or, and this is probably the most effective way, he can suggest that a small group take a problem, work on it for a time and report back. These problems and their elucidation and proposed solutions must be kept very close to real village situations, otherwise they become mere academic exercises;

(4) The Mission found an almost complete dearth of case studies relating to community development and social change in India. The Mission was aware of the slowly increasing number of contemporary village studies by Indian and foreign sociologists and anthropologists, but they are still very few, and do not appear to be used imaginatively in training courses. Yet these studies provide the kind of village material round which teaching and discussion should be planned to give it a realistic and not an idealistic slant, and should be used in orientation courses, extension courses, and *Panchayat* training camps.

IN-SERVICE TRAINING

In-service training is the training given after the individual remains on his job for some time and needs re-orientation of ideas and some new knowledge. Periodical in-service training is necessary because the worker remaining absorbed in his work, gets little time to keep himself abreast with the latest trends and developments, and this needs to be recouped with fresh ideas and knowledge.

The main objectives of the in-service training are:

(*i*) To re-orient the attitudes and skills of the extension worker and to re-equip him to tackle problems in a better way.

(*ii*) To remove doubts and difficulties being experienced by the extension worker (trainee) in the field.

(*iii*) To impart detailed knowledge and experience about programmes:

In which people want the extension worker to have better knowledge.

In which the extension worker himself thinks he is deficient.

In which the senior members of the staff and officers think the extension workers are deficient.

(*iv*) To pool experiences of the workers for mutual advantage through group discussions, staff meetings and seminars.

(*v*) To give them advanced training in latest researches, techniques, and methods.

(*vi*) To develop in them the capacity to plan their work in accordance with the special needs, circumstances and resources of the people concerned.

(*vii*) To develop initiative.

In the first two objectives, preparation has to be made before the commencement of the training programme by collecting necessary material. Necessary notes on all material points should be kept ready from before. While preparing these notes, it will be necessary to consult the concerned experts and specialists for help in preparing answers to all doubts, difficulties and problems reported from various levels. Attempt has to be made to answer them, with a positive and a definite answer. Unless these answers are positive and definite, the trainees would not be satisfied.

For the pooling of experiences, staff meetings, seminars, group discussions, study tours to research stations and successful projects in villages of the same block, district and state and outside are necessary. Besides, the case histories of successful projects should be carefully collected and circulated. A discourse by specialists, successful leaders and field workers on the occasion of the staff meetings, seminars or group discussions are also quite useful.

Organisation of meetings with the specialists and others should be with a clear and definite objective of getting new knowledge or of solving a particular problem. It is better to discuss a few items thoroughly than to rush through a heavy agenda. The composition of such meetings should not be very heterogeneous because it will be difficult to develop identity of purpose and common interest. Although heterogeneity sometimes helps in a better comradeship, co-ordination and mutual understanding of each others point of view, it reduces many meetings and seminars to almost a non-serious affair. Heterogeneous elements being more or less uninterested in several subjects, sit unattentively and start talking in groups and leave and join the discussions periodically by going out and coming in for mental relaxation and relieving boredom.

DEFICIENCY AND PROFICIENCY CHARTS

A deficiency and proficiency chart should be maintained for each worker by the immediate officer concerned. A copy of this chart should be sent to the officer in-charge, in-service training, well in advance so that he may chalk out his plan of training in such a way as to be able to meet specific deficiencies.

FREQUENCY OF IN-SERVICE TRAINING

Frequency of in-service training depends upon the calibre of workers available and the requirements of the job. In-service training to be effective has to be a continuous process in some form or the other and, therefore, no definite period can be fixed for it.

GUIDANCE PROVIDED BY THE SENIORS AND COLLEAGUES

Guidance from seniors and colleagues helps a great deal in removing deficiencies and developing necessary skill and attitude. A good worker should be keen to seek guidance when he is in doubt or feels hesitant.

Guidance is most effective when it is ungrudgingly given, in a spirit of friendliness at an appropriate time so that it could be taken advantage of effectively. It is of help when it is practical and is based on actual experience and knowledge, otherwise it tends to be theoretical. The bureaucratic attitude of mere fault finding does not provide guidance. This is amply supported by the experience gained in respect of community development programme, started in the country in 1952. Most of the field level workers were trained in extension methods before it started. They tried to practise these methods in the field, but they could not continue to do so for long on account of the improper attitude of most of the immediate and superior officers who had not received any training in extension methods nor had they any experience of such work. Had they been trained from before, the subordinate workers would have continued to shape well.

The attitude or behaviour of the higher officers towards their subordinates and the approach they have towards field problems has a great bearing on the attitude of the subordinates. If their approach is dogmatic and purely subjective, the subordinates also develop the same approach or attitude in course of time. Stress on visible achievements and physical targets without making the subordinates a party to the planning of the programmes results in showy and superficial work. The worker in these circumstances ceases to be an extension agent. He is concerned only with carrying out orders, and earning appreciation without doing solid work.

BUILDING UP AND GUIDING WORKERS

It is a solemn duty of those in superior position to build up workers in their charge. They cannot discharge their duty unless they develop objectivity, understanding and a sympathe-tic attitude, and keep their knowledge up to date. There is a case history which illustrates this point. There was a block development officer who was not considered to be a good worker. The regional officer concerned during the course of his visit found that he had not prepared any block and family plans. He was annoyed, and he reprimanded the worker severely. The block development officer said "Sir, everybody who comes to the block orders things to be done, but nobody gives any gui-dance. I do not know how to make a block or a family plan. I have, therefore, not been able to make them. Would you kindly teach me how to prepare them?"

The regional officer had himself no practice in preparing these plans. He had, however, given some thought to the problem. The remarks of the block development officer so much pinched him that he immediately sat with the block development officer and started telling him how to make a block and a family plan. Himself without practice, it took him several hours, but he did it. This gave a very good practice to him as well as to the block development officer. The block development officer after learning how to make a plan called the village level workers, taught them how to prepare family plans and got all the plans completed in a short period. This block ultimately became the best block of the district. The block development officer got good character roll entries and was ultimately selected for a higher post on the basis of his good work.

EXTENSION WORKER'S OWN EXPERIENCE

No man learns more than through his own desire to learn, from situations and circumstances in which he is placed. No experience can be more practical than what is gained through one's own efforts. A child tries to catch the flame of the lamp but once he burns his fingers, he never attempts to catch it again. Similar is the case with every individual, group or community all of whom try to learn by experience. Learning may be positive or negative, but whatever it is, it is an experience to be taken advantage of in future.

The extension worker also learns in the same way, and as he goes on learning and gathering experience from his failures and successes, he becomes better equipped to do his job more efficiently.

DIFFERENT ROLES OF THE EXTENSION WORKER

The extension worker has different roles while working for agricultural and community development programmes. These roles are:

(a) As a planner.
(b) As an organiser.
(c) As a catalyser.
(d) As a leader.
(e) As a friend.
(f) As an enabler.
(g) As an expert.
(h) As a co-ordinator.
(i) As an evaluator.
(j) As a researcher.

Each of these roles is very important from the extension point of view. The extension worker has not only to work in each of these roles to be fully effective but has also to learn and gather experience from each of them.

(a) As a planner

The extension worker as a planner has to study and analyse the local situation, needs and resources and then plan out and finalise action programmes. This is a very important role for, unless work is carried out according to a pre-determined plan, confusion and difficulty in its execution is likely to come up.

Planning for action is a difficult, complicated and integrated process. It requires a careful study of the social structure—group formations, habits, customs, traditions and behaviours, economic conditions, stage of development, *etc.*, of the community. It requires knowledge of the methods by which similar plans and programmes were accepted before. There should also be a correct idea of the financial implications of the plan and the resources available for the purpose. If these are wanting, the plan is likely to fizzle out.

No rigid rules can be laid down for planning. It always begins with a set of circumstances in terms of people which vary greatly from situation to situation. It means starting with the appraisal of the situation, making of an estimate as to where one has to begin, with what objectives, with what resources, with what limiting conditions, *etc.* Planning as it is conceived today, represents the whole act from the studying of the problem to the action taken to solve that problem. It is therefore, not only mere development of a solution, but also development of a solution in relation to a given problem in a given social environment and active application of that solution.

As a planner, the extension worker has to pay attention to the following:

(*i*) Identification of the problem;
(*ii*) Implications of the problem;
(*iii*) Solution of the problem; and
(*iv*) Action programme.

(*i*) *Identification of the problem*

Clear identification of the problem is the first stage in planning. The item looks simple, but it is of vital importance and should be very carefully gone into.

Identification of the problem depends upon appraisal of the local situation in respect of the community, resources and potentialities of the area or the people.

Many a time the problem is not what it appears to be. Taking an example of the programme of composting, stress is being mainly laid on digging of compost pits, filling them with refuse and making compost. This is done with the idea of producing more of organic manure. The programme of composting looks so simple as above, but it is not really what has been described and generally understood by the so-called general run of the field workers.

The primary problems in composting are, in fact, dearth of fuel for cooking and inadequate supply of organic matter for composting. Unless these two problems are tackled by planting more trees for fuel or by providing coal and producing additional organic manure, people are not likely to take up composting seriously.

This example has been given to show that often what transpires to be a problem is not a problem in reality, but it is the resultant problem of some other basic problem which needs to be tackled earlier than the resultant problem. If action on the resultant problem is taken up earlier than the basic problem, lot of time, energy and money of the people and the agency sponsoring the programme is wasted. Identification of the problem at the start, therefore, is very vital to the programme itself. Hence its great importance.

(ii)   Implications of the problem

Even if the problem has been well defined, a detailed study of its nature, manner, scope and implications is necessary. The problem may look simple, but it may have very deep ramifications.

To refer again to the example of composting, the problem has very deep ramifications, deep in the sense that the programme is very seriously affected by various social, economic and traditional factors with the result that it is difficult to execute it in a simple way. The work of composting is mainly carried out by women-folk. It is they who are to be mainly approached for it. The women-folk would not like to carry huge loads of cattle refuse to far off places. They, therefore, dump it near the village '*abadi*' into heaps. This is a social problem arising from age old habits and customs of the people. The families do not utilise all the excreta for composting. Quite a part of it has to be converted into dung cakes to be used as fuel. This is an economic problem which has got to be tackled for making the programme a success.

There is a habit of *Hookah* smoking and the method of *ghee* making which require the use of dung cakes. These have also to be changed, by suggesting suitable alternative measures.

It would appear from the above that not only it is necessary to be clear about the problem, but it should also be discovered as to how it is connected with other problems and situations which are not usually apparent.

These other problems and situations should be studied before starting to implement the programme.

(iii) Solution of the problem

The next step in planning is to find out the solution for the problem. It depends on:

(a) Past experiences of the people/community;

(b) Personal experiences of the extension worker based on survey and his past experiences of similar or allied problems elsewhere;

(c) Advice of the technical experts based on their past experiences or researches; and

(d) Attitude of the people in nearby communities if the solution is such that it affects them also.

The people with all their experience know the solution of most of their problems, but are not able to implement it on account of lack of resources, confidence, unity among themselves and absence of a motivating force. In some cases they need outside technical advice, resources or motivating force. How the people want to solve their problems should always receive prior consideration by the extension worker. Their views and experiences should be examined by the extension worker and a suitable line of action should be worked out.

There may be more than one solution to a particular problem. In such cases, a simple solution easy to be implemented and well within the available resources should be attempted. Unanimous agreement in respect of all issues is not often possible among the members of the community. This may delay the action. In such cases, the extension worker should not rush through the plan, but try to wait and attempt for an unanimous or near unanimous agreement. These may sometimes delay the execution of the plan but it is worth while waiting for an agreement among the people. People are usually open to correction and that is a favourable factor. Unanimous decision about a solution is necessary to avoid unhappy consequences and situations.

Sometimes people come to an agreement, but do not maintain that agreement afterwards. All individuals tend to be driven
by conflicting motives and this produces considerable inconsistencies in behaviour which make an individual support an idea
once and speak with reservations about it thereafter. Not only,
therefore, is an agreed solution necessary to be secured, but it
is also necessary to maintain the agreement by reiterating the
basic points of view leading to the decision and removing doubts
if any.

Individuals who agree to the plan or the proposal at the start,
sometimes try to resist it afterwards because they develop doubts
about the wisdom of their own agreement. Such doubts generally take the form of resistance to action, petty arguments over
small points in the plan, search for scapegoats and unnecessary
criticism of someone in the group or outside or of the extension worker.

As a planner, the extension worker specially feels the difficulty when more than one community is concerned with the
solution and the solution is such that it only benefits one community and affects another in some way or the other. In such
cases, the extension worker has to approach both the communities and get their agreement. A typical example is the problem
of water-logging in several parts of the country. There are
various villages which are seriously affected by this problem.
They like to construct a drain but the people of the neighbouring community do not allow the drain to be constructed through
their village, for they feel that they are likely to suffer by such
a move.

(iv) Action programme

The final phase of planning relates to execution. After a
proper solution of the problem has been decided upon, one is
required to plan a detailed action programme. Failure to plan
an action programme carefully results in what is called the
'Boomerang' effect which recoils on the planner himself.

Processing and finalisation of the action programme should
always be carried out democratically through the participation
of the leaders of the people, of the entire extension staff and

others who can make some contribution. It should then be approved by the people at large. Association of the above personnel in the finalisation of the action programme is essential. A large number of failures in programmes can be attributed to lack of association of the people and the concerned workers, with the processing and finalisation of the action programme.

The main steps for planning an action programme are:

(a) Listing activities by which the objective already decided upon can be achieved.

(b) Fixing priorities for different activities.

(c) Phasing the programme in a well co-ordinated manner in relation to time and resources by fixing goals and targets.

(d) Selection of key personnel and defining their individual and group responsibility for each activity in the plan.

(e) Training and building up their attitudes.

(f) Preparing and educating the members of the community in the programme.

(g) Planning and arranging supplies and services:

  (i) Assessment of available resources.

  (ii) Estimation of the resources likely to be available from outside and making them available in time.

(h) Continuous review and evaluation of means, results and progress towards achievement of the objectives.

(i) Preparation of plans for an additional period of time.

Each of the above steps is important in its own way and cannot be neglected. Neglect of even one of them means that to that extent the plan will be defective.

(b) *As an organiser*

The extension worker in the role of an organiser has to be fully conversant with the plan of action. He has to know his personnel fully, keep their morale high, gather their reactions through staff meetings, seminars, and personal contacts. He should guide and build them, periodically exchange views with them and establish cordial relationship between him and his seniors, juniors and colleagues. He has to anticipate the likely reactions of the community and take steps to counteract them. He has to arrange the required supplies and services in advance, study and remove bottle-necks, keep to objectives, evaluate and change strategy with each assessment. He has to make the best use of the available resources of men, money and materials and check all leakage and wastage of these resources.

Organising ability is a trait not present in all individuals. Those who possess this trait are bound to succeed. A plan may be perfect, but if one does not possess organising skill and ability for execution, it does not succeed.

A good organiser seldom orders things to be done except in rare circumstances. He promotes his plan through by means of personal discussion, emotional approach, proper education and guidance and by taking into confidence his colleagues, workers, and group of community leaders and recalcitrant elements in the community. He guides and influences their thinking.

A good organiser spots out the key persons in advance, trains and builds them up, shapes their attitudes properly, defines their responsibility and motivates them to shoulder responsibility, reposes confidence and works as a member of the team.

A good organiser is responsible for all follow-up action. One of the common defects these days, is that programmes are started but they are not followed to the finish with the result that the work carried out with great sacrifice of time, labour and money, is wasted. Continuity of action is one of the greatest qualities of an extension worker. This is a difficult task, nevertheless necessary, especially in these days when thinking goes a sudden change with change in personnel manning the programmes.

An organiser sees things in broad prospective, listens to all, collects information from different sources and then takes a balanced view. Many workers are good organisers, but are not able to take a balanced view of things because their vision becomes blurred due to rumblings in petty matters, group rivalries, caste considerations, favouritism, *etc.* Such persons succeed for some time but ultimately end in failure as a result of strong opposition from their own colleagues, subordinates or the members of the community.

Mention has been made above of the emotional approach. It has been found that implementation of the plans succeeds better if some kind of emotional touch is given to the programmes. This is necessary because it is through this approach mainly that the community can be held together. Only when emotional feelings are aroused, people develop oneness of purpose, forget differences and work with some kind of unconscious motivation. In olden times, the entire development programme specially in South India was carried out through the temples in which the people had faith and confidence. These temples distributed food to the poor, got tanks dug for irrigation, and hospitals and dispensaries constructed. As people had faith in these institutions, they did whatever they were asked to do.

(c) As a catalyser

Just as a catalyser is needed to expedite the pace of a chemical reaction, an extension worker is needed as a catalytic agent to initiate thinking and get the ball rolling for a change in the community/village or the people at large. It is a very difficult role to perform nevertheless very useful and necessary, for catalytic reactions disturb and change the course of thinking completely.

Every worker is not suitable and so every time is not opportunate for pushing an idea through. One has to see and watch for moments when the individuals or the people are slightly more receptive for drilling through an innovation bringing motion into the cesspool of stagnation.

Often people realise the benefits of a particular idea, but they do not adopt it for some reason or the other. If anybody approaches and questions them, they seem to pretend that they know all about it, but when asked why they do not adopt it they say "Now Sir, the village level worker or the assistant development officer or you have told us, we will do it from next year." When next year comes they repeat the same. Thus it goes on. A catalytic action is necessary to motivate and initiate reaction in the people for adoption of the improved practices. This reaction can be initiated, besides many other things, by demonstrations and films, through study tours and by providing prompt assistance when they feel baffled by any situation.

Study tours help a great deal in accelerating mental reactions. There is an example of a farmer who went to see the Bhakra Nangal Dam on a sight-seeing tour. He was very much awed to see the dam, its utility and the vast reservoir of water stored there. After the visit, he remarked "I never realised that the construction of *bunds* or *dams* is so useful a proposition. I unnecessarily opposed the idea of constructing a bund in my village. I would after return to my village now see that the bund which is half constructed, is immediately completed.

In an extension block, the paddy crop was being continually attacked by gundhy bug every year. The village level worker approached the villagers and told them that the malady was controllable but they did not believe him. He immediately demonstrated the control measures. The pest was killed and the damage saved. This entirely changed the course of thinking of the villagers and the majority of them asked for the control measures to be carried out. The demonstration at a psychological moment convinced the villagers of the utility of control measures. At any other time no amount of reasoning would have done the trick. Thus, the programme got to a good start. The extension worker should always try to select such psychological moments for initiating new schemes and imparting new ideas.

Another example of motivation through a catalytic action can be cited of a village in Faridpur block of Bareilly district in Uttar Pradesh in which a local leader was initiated to action when the block development officer read a report in one of the block development committee meetings giving details of the work done by different *Gaon Sabhas* of the block. To his surprise, the local leader discovered that his own *Gaon Sabha* had not done anything and was the last in the ladder. The block development officer also added a little sarcastic salt to the mental agony of this leader and as the result he felt so much ashamed of his position that immediately after reaching his village, he collected all the key men of the village and exhorted them to see that their village was the best next time in the entire block. The impersonal remark of the block development officer at the committee meeting so much moved this leader that he went from house to house and contacted each family of the village and initiated them to action by providing them necessary guidance and inspiration. He also got himself trained as *Gram Sahayak* (village leader). The result was that his village stood first in the *Kharif* campaign of 1959, as the best village of the block and won a prize.

(d) As a leader

In the role of a leader, the extension worker has to lead the people amongst whom he works by giving them proper guidance, solving their difficulties and inculcating in them a spirit of co-operative thinking and working for their individual or common good. He has to be the torch-bearer for showing them the path they have to tread in order to achieve their goal. They may tumble down and lose courage in their march, but he has to make them stand up again and encourage them to work harder than before with self-confidence.

The leader has to guide the people in a way that they with his help are able to identify their own needs and find out the methods to fulfil these needs entirely by their own resources or partly with their own resources and partly with the resources made available to them by an outside agency.

The extension worker in this role should not force any decision or programme on the people, but on the other hand, he should create in them a lively interest by encouraging discussions, asking pertinent questions to initiate thinking, showing demonstrations or films and arranging study tours. All these should be done with a definite purpose and motive so that the people study things themselves.

At times, it may fall to the lot of the extension worker, in his role as a guide to impose a decision or interfere or use undue influence or take over the responsibility of conducting the project himself or give the existing project a pace. Such a course, although necessary at times should not be continued for long as the extension worker by so doing, would be defeating his own purpose. It has to be clearly borne in mind that during the period the responsibility is taken away from the community/ village, the process of learning and growth and development in the community/village is either stopped or reduced and this ultimately delays the adoption of the programme.

Leadership is of two types, namely direct leadership and indirect leadership. They are discussed in detail below:

(i) *Direct leadership*

The extension worker at times due to force of circumstances assumes the role of a direct leader and passes on his ideas to the people for adoption. They adopt them on account of sheer respect for him or on account of fear of his official position or in the hope of getting some future benefit from him. Such a leadership may result in some temporary good and success, but is not lasting and self-perpetuating. The whole enterprise in such a case remains to be the show of the extension worker rather than of the people/community itself.

The extension worker in the role of a direct leader often tries to take full credit for the success of the project and whenever an outside visitor or his immediate superior officers come to visit the work, he tries to show it as the work done by him. If the work is good and is appreciated by the visitor, he is acclaimed to be a good worker. Such an acclamation satisfies the vanity of the worker but weans him away from the people.

When the extension worker assumes the role of a direct leader, people may or may not be initiated to action by their own self-propelling desire which must be created in them before making the programme a success. Usually in such circumstances, people adopt a programme only temporarily without being motivated and without putting their heart into it. The people in such cases lapse to the original state as soon as the extension worker assuming the role of a direct leader, is transferred or leaves the community for some reason. Success of programmes in such cases entirely depends upon the extension worker who, out of enthusiasm for the good of the community and in more cases for his own good, for the sake of pleasing his higher officers, or for getting promotion or good character role entries, goes out of his way to persuade the community to undertake or adopt certain programmes. There are also examples of adoption of the programmes by the community through direct leadership. but success in such cases is mostly the result of continued efforts for several years.

Once when I was travelling with a high dignitary in the district of Bulandshahr (Uttar Pradesh), I was suddenly asked by him to take him to a village which he might have visited before. Luckily the village which he had visited about a year before was only two miles from the place. He found to his surprise that its condition was deplorable. The drains were dirty, the wells were surrounded with filth with flies breeding in it, the bricks of the pavement had given way at places leaving space filled with filth and mud, compost pits had given way to piles of manure, and the urinals constructed a year ago were not being used, *etc.* The distinguished visitor was shocked to see the condition of this village. Such is the plight of scores of villages which are made show-pieces by enthusiastic workers who spend large sums of money without creating an urge for improvement in the people. Distinguished persons come and go but the villages remain where they were except for minor material changes in the shape of sanitary wells, bath rooms, urinals, *etc.*, which are also not used properly by the people after the visit of the dignitary is over. The essential thing is change in the attitude of the people. The attitude did not change as the result of the extension workers' insistence on the programme to please the visiting dignitaries. The visit of a high dignitary is taken by the village leaders as a prestige programme for the village and thus they also join the extension worker and his officers to make the village a show-piece and arrange a tea, lunch or dinner party in honour of the dignitary. There may be some apparent pleasure and satisfaction in such programmes, but they result in a sort of unholy alliance between the village leaders and the extension worker in which each tries to help or benefit the other at the cost of people. The relationship in such cases is between the village leaders (not representing the feeling and aspirations of the common men) and the extension workers and not between the common mass of people in the village and the extension worker. The growth of such undesirable relationship between the extension worker and the local leaders who are mostly opportunist, is detrimental to the cause of extension of agricultural and community development programmes and has to be discouraged. At present this is the one major factor which is coming in the way of the success of these programmes and the sooner this tendency is checked the better it would be.

Direct leadership on the part of the extension worker is sometimes necessary when there is deep apathy in the people towards programmes. It pays dividends in some cases, provided the extension worker after assuming the role of a direct leader passes on that leadership to the community/village leaders and generates in them a desire to change. Such instances are there, but they are rare.

The extension worker is sometimes compelled to assume direct leadership. One of the reasons why he does so is that his superior or higher officers try to seek quick results. Direct leadership is no doubt the best for getting quick results, but such apparent success may be more a show than real adoption of the programme by the people with necessary conviction behind it. Our ultimate object is to leave the community better and stronger than what we find it at the commencement of our work. The real test of successful extension is to be found in what abides after the extension worker ceases to be on the scene. If a genuine and lasting enthusiasm is generated by him, the community or its leaders will make their own plans to start new programmes for their betterment. The very first successful project under such conditions leads the people to undertake further improvement without much external stimulus.

(ii) Indirect leadership

As against direct leadership, there is indirect leadership in which the extension worker, although he leads the people actually, works behind the scene through people's own leaders whom he selects very carefully on the basis of their qualities rather than on any other consideration. If he chooses wrong leaders, the programme does not expand as people in the long run follow a leader who contributes something and abandon those who do not contribute anything. A leader in order to justify his position must contribute something towards the betterment of the community and if he does not, he would cease to enjoy that position.

The extension worker in this kind of leadership has constantly to try to build the people and its leaders rather than make himself more and more important and indispensable. He should not accept any office or assume any power and prestige. He has to provide inspiration, guidance, technical knowledge and skill and bring together different leaders in the community/village to think for the betterment of the entire community/village.

There is an inherent desire in the majority of the persons responsible for running the programmes to assume the role of direct leadership. Such persons always try to run the programmes on behalf of their organisation or their government in the same way as *Zamindars* used to manage their *Zamindaris*. They do not allow the people to do things for themselves but make them dependent on their organisation even for things which they can manage themselves provided they are given proper knowledge and training. These people forget that not only do such tendencies increase the organisation's or government's expenditure but result in a lot of complaints and assumption of unnecessary responsibility, difficult to shoulder. Taking over the responsibility of jobs which people cannot undertake for want of specialised knowledge and skill or large amount of capital, sounds commonsense, but undertaking those jobs which people could easily undertake by proper training and guidance, stands in the way of people making their own efforts, developing their ideas and using their ingenuity.

(e) As a friend

The extension worker in the role of a friend has to be one

with the entire community rather than with a group. He has to resist all attempts by one group to own him or to capture his attention to the exclusion of others. He has to establish good relations with all the groups in the community/village and bring diverse groups together so that they may take collective decisions to solve common problems. If he does not function as a friend of all, he cannot function effectively in the villages. He has, therefore, to be a friend of all always ready to help irrespective of any consideration. He has to be a warm and friendly person, sensitive to the deeper feelings of the people and interested in the little things that are important in the lives of individuals, groups or community. Often it is these little things that create confidence in the people towards the extension worker. By participating in all their joys and sorrows, their religious and socio-cultural functions and by providing medical and first aid to the sick and the injured, an extension worker can earn the goodwill of the village people.

Many extension workers complain that they are not able to play this role of a friend effectively as they live in a rented house in the village of their posting. If this house belongs to some influential person, the extension worker is unnecessarily identified with the group to which his landlord belongs. Such circumstances are often beyond the control of the extension worker. It is necessary to make adequate arrangements so that he may be independent of any body's help or obligation so far as his personal needs are concerned.

The people view the extension worker with great suspicion when he goes to the village and contacts them for the first time. Before he starts functioning effectively he has to create an atmosphere in which he is taken to be a friend by every villager. In course of time he starts contacting individuals and tries to gain their confidence and friendship. A very good account of this contact has been published by Sri Laxmi Lal Shah Jagati, village level worker of Salt block, district Almora in the November 1959 issue of the *Gram Sewak*. He has reported that as soon as he got his new posting orders as a village level worker, he was given a target of planting 2000 trees in his area, by the assistant development officer (agriculture). When he reached the village, nobody listened to him. He even called a meeting of the village people, explained to them the programme and requested them to give their indents for seeds and seedlings. Nobody paid any attention to his request. This depressed and perplexed him very much. He roamed about for 18 days continuously in his circle without any success. During this period he tried to collect the village children on each one of his tours and told them a few tit-bit stories, engaged them in simple plays and recited some songs, *etc.* This attracted them and in course of time the children started gathering around him whenever he visited a village. This affection of the children towards the extension worker attracted the attention and sympathy of the villagers and made them change their suspicion into confidence. Eventually he succeeded in establishing individual and group contacts with the village people and in getting a chance to talk about the programme. This worker later on also tried to bring the two rival parties in the village together by suggesting the idea of planting a community orchard for the benefit of the village. He ultimately succeeded in his efforts.

One example of 'little things' that matter in winning the confidence of the people can be cited of the lady principal of a school in Lucknow. While presenting the annual report of her school on the occasion of the late Mr. Nehru's birthday celebration which also happened to be a children's day, she mentioned with great warmth, the contribution of the school *mali,* a low paid servant, in beautifying the school compound. Such references in the annual reports of even the lowest paid men win their support and heart. When I casually talked to the *mali* the next day on my way to the office, he said "Sir, our principal is a very kind-hearted lady and we all love her as our mother."

(f) *As an enabler*

The extension worker in this role helps to expedite adoption of programmes step by step through an educational process, by providing material facilities and creating psychological conditions necessary to bring about the desired change.

Amongst the material facilities are supplies needed for executing a programme. If a new fertilizer is to be popularised, the extension worker, after convincing the people in the use of the new fertilizer, has to arrange for its supplies to be made available locally or at a central place in good time before it is required for application in the field. If the extension worker does not enable the people to get the supplies or is not able to arrange for a source of supply—governmental, co-operative or private, the programme fails to expand. This role of the extension worker is very important for many a time the programmes fail on account of lack of material assistance. Programmes also fail or are delayed on account of lack of inadequate material assistance.

Should supplies be made available in the village itself or at the existing centres of supplies as co-operative unions or governmental seedstores? Either system can be adopted but arranging supplies in the village itself is more convenient. If the method of arranging supplies at the village level is adopted once, it should be continued in subsequent years also. If this is not done, the programme in most cases does not succeed, because people remain in the hope that the supplies would be delivered to them in the village itself and therefore, do not try to get them from the nearest seedstore or the block headquarters. When supplies are required to be brought from outside the village, it is essential to tell the people about their source and persuade them right from the very beginning to get them individually or collectively as a group or community/village as a whole.

People have been known to give up an improved practice even when they come to like it, if the extension worker fails to enable them to continue to adopt the practice arranging the required supplies in time or telling them when and where to get them from. In Vidyapeeth block of Varanasi district of Uttar Pradesh, a few farmers on the advice of the extension worker tried the application of superphosphate to their potato crops with good results. These fields were shown by the extension worker to other farmers, who were also very much impressed by the results of the application of fertilizers. But when the farmers wanted to apply superphosphate to their potato crops next year, they found that there was no stock at the seedstore. The result was that they could not apply superphosphate that year although they were convinced about its utility. Unfortunately, this happened in the subsequent year also and thus two years passed off without application of superphosphate to their potato crops. This delayed the adoption of the practice by two years.

In the psychological role of an enabler, the extension worker enables the community/village to move to the desired goal by creating such psychological conditions which expedite the process of education of the community/village in the utility of the programme and intensify their desire to bring about a change. This psychological atmosphere can be created by the extension worker by stimulating discussions in the village/community, by showing demonstrations, by taking the people on study tours, by bringing people in contact with others who have already adopted the desired improved practice and gained experience.

(g) As an expert

The extension worker as an expert is responsible for advising on methods, showing things by doing them himself, helping in identifying local problems such as of pests and diseases, *etc.*, and finding out their solutions himself or with the help of higher experts. He should have a working knowledge of day-to-day problems of the community/village and their solutions.

The extension worker at the village level cannot be an expert on all subjects, but as problems get unfolded he has to know more and more about them so as to be able to guide the community/village. If he does not possess the working knowledge of any particular problem of the village/area he should know whom to approach for it. As soon as such a problem comes to be known and he is unable to suggest any solution, he should immediately approach the expert concerned for the solution.

Knowledge of successful projects elsewhere

The extension worker in his role as an expert has to be very wide awake to find out successful projects in every community/village and then to arrange study tours or take the message of successful projects to the community/village where that problem exists.   —

He has to be fed continually with new extension and technical literature so that he may refresh his knowledge to suit to local problems. There should be arrangements at the block, district, state or central level to communicate this new knowledge to the extension workers at every level in the shortest possible time. Arrangements should also be made to supply him with the latest extension literature, magazines, papers, bulletins, *etc.*

Expertness in programmes

Perfection in technical skill comes more by experience and by actually doing the job. A farmer once remarked in a seminar held in 1959 at Loni (district Meerut) that difficulties are there at every step but when one plunges into work, solutions to his difficulties begin dawning upon him and when this happens, he soon becomes an expert. It is for this reason, he said, that everybody should try to do things himself before he is in a position to advise and suggest practical solutions. This advice of the farmer has to be followed by all workers.

Many programmes look apparently very simple and, therefore, instructions are issued to the field workers from the headquarters as a matter of routine without considering the full implications. This must be avoided. Programmes, however simple they may be, require some kind of expert handling and guidance. Gandhiji once said to Ba, "I have eaten *Bajra*[1] Chapaties (bread) made by several ladies, but I have never found them so tasty and sweet as those prepared by you". This was not only a compliment to Ba, but a truth for, howsoever simple it

[1] Bajra (Pennisetum glaucum L Sand H) is a small millet grown widely in India.

may be to prepare *Bajra Chapaties,* everybody could not make them so tasty and sweet as Ba did. What is that which makes them more tasty and more sweet, is the expert touch which Ba had. All extension workers have to arm themselves with that expert 'Ba' touch by working programmes themselves and then afterwards teaching others.

(*h*) As a co-ordinater

The extension worker in the role of a co-ordinater has to be a patient listener and a firm negotiater and at the same time strong enough to push his ideas through. He has to work behind the scene without showing his importance. He has to work in a way that others realise their role and help him in fulfilling his mission or objective.

The extension worker in this role has to work along with his colleagues by making a common cause with their programmes in a way that the work is carried out with co-ordinated approach with a view to getting the maximum benefit, over a period of time. This is a very difficult role which everybody cannot play successfully. The main guiding points which can make this role a success are outlined below:

(*i*) Avoid criticising those with whom you have to work.

(*ii*) Everybody has his own point of view and it may be that there is something in his point of view also which one does not know unless it is discussed over fully. One should, therefore, listen more to what others say and talk less.

(*iii*) Try to bring round your colleagues to your point of view across the table by convincing them. Do not argue if they do not have an open mind and are not receptive.

If the colleagues try to stick to their incorrect views, argument need not be continued, but they should be allowed time to see things for themselves and become wiser.

(*iv*) Find out the greatest common measure of agreement and then press your point of view further and go on repeating till you succeed. If other colleagues have something to offer, it must be immediately accepted.

If one is sincere and feels that what one believes in is fundamentally correct, there is no reason why one should not be able to succeed in one's mission.

There is hardly any Agricultural and Community Development programme which an extension worker can claim to handle single-handed and, therefore, it is necessary for him to take other colleagues of his also into confidence and to induce them to realise their part and carry it out. This can be illustrated by the programme of popularising application of fertilizers to crop. The programme involves the following action steps and concerns the agencies given below:

Action steps	*Department concerned*
Demonstrations	agriculture and community development departments and commercial firms
Submission of timely indent	agriculture and co-operative departments and the co-operatives
Timely supply	agriculture and co-operative departments and the co-operatives
Proper storage	agriculture department and co-operatives
Timely distribution of Co-operative credit	agriculture and co-operative departments, co-operative banks and service co-operatives
Correct method of application.	agriculture and community development departments.

It would appear from the above that several agencies are involved in the programme of popularising fertilizers.

Technically, the item comes under the purview of the agriculture department, but co-operatives, community development and co-operative departments and commercial firms dealing with fertilizers are no less concerned with programme than the agriculture department and, therefore, if the specialist in agriculture does not co-ordinate this programme with all the concerned agencies, it is bound to suffer a great deal. It would succeed only if all the workers belonging to the concerned departments or agencies work together with a common objective. The same could be said about many other programmes.

(i) As an evaluator

In the role of an evaluator, the extension worker has to analyse the relative roles and contributions of individuals, groups and communities and make a critical study of programmes and the means, and methods employed to execute them. In fact he has to study and determine from time to time the degree of success achieved towards the attainment of fundamental objectives, to appraise the effectiveness of the organisation, means and techniques, pinpointing their strong and weak spots and the reasons thereof and finally finding out the extent and nature of changes to be introduced in them, so that the set objectives may be achieved within the desired time.

Evaluation by the extension worker should be carried out against the background of local situation, social customs and traditions, religious beliefs, habits, and economic, institutional and leadership patterns in the people. As the acceptance of the programme by the people depends a great deal upon these factors, it is also necessary to evaluate the effect of the programme upon these factors and also to find out how far they necessitate changes and adjustments to be made in the programmes themselves so that they could fit in the local socio-cultural, religious, economic, institutional and leadership patterns of the community/village.

Evaluation in stages

The extension worker has to evaluate all his programmes in three stages:

(i) Before the programme is started, so as to establish a bench mark for judging further progress;

(ii) While the programme is in operation; and

(iii) After the programme has been completed.

Of these three stages, stage (*ii*) has to be a continuing process till the programme is finally adopted or completed. Evaluation during the operation of the programme is very essential and such a study helps a great deal in correcting mistakes,
adopting better means, methods and techniques and accelerating
the pace of the programmes.

Survey and determining a bench mark before the start of the
programme are a very important pre-requisite which should
not be forgotten. Very often in a hurry, this aspect is
lost sight of. Determining a bench mark, and planning
the programme on the basis of a bench mark, survey takes some
time but the time spent in this work brings in rich dividends
later.

Agency for evaluation

Programmes can be evaluated or assessed by the extension
worker himself or got evaluated by an outside agency. The evaluation by an outside agency is independent, objective and un-
biased, while the evaluation by the extension worker himself can
be biased, and more subjective than objective. Although evaluation from an outside agency indirectly connected with the programme is desirable, self-evaluation by the worker himself is also
very valuable and important. It should be a *must* with each
extension worker. Unless he is in the habit of evaluating his
own performance, it would not be possible for him to improve his thinking and method of working. Evaluation has to
be considered by him as an impetus to improvement and as a
safeguard against persistence in error. It has to be done by
him through everyday observation, informal and formal studies
and by measuring both the tangible and intangible, quantitative
and qualitative, physical or psychological gains or losses in a
certain programme.

Evaluation in terms of objectives

Evaluation by an extension worker has to be done in terms
of the objectives of the programme. The objectives are of three
kinds:

(*i*) Fundamental objectives
(*ii*) Specific objectives
(*iii*) Working objectives

Fundamental objectives are determined or set out first. These are followed by the specific and working objectives. This order is reversed in attaining them. Working objectives are always attained first and are followed by the specific and fundamental objectives. An illustration of the programme of food production in a certain village of Sarojininagar block of Lucknow district (Uttar Pradesh) can be cited to explain it clearly. Three objectives of this programme are described below:

(*i*) *Fundamental objectives*

Increase in food production by 40 per cent, that is, 65.4 tons during the Third Five-Year Plan period over the production of 157.5 tons in 1960-61 (end of Second Five-Year Plan).

(*ii*) *Specific objectives*

The fundamental objectives would be achieved through the following specific objectives:

	Additional food production
(1) Bringing additional area under irrigation	24.20 Tonnes
(2) Improved seeds	5.00 ,,
(3) Manures and fertilizers	47.00 ,,
(4) Improved agricultural practices	9.60 ,,
(5) Land reclamation	3.20 ,,
(6) Soil Conservation	10.00 ,,
(7) Controlling pests and diseases	4.00 ,,
	103.00 Tonnes

(*iii*) *Working objectives*

The fundamental and specific objectives would be achieved through the fulfilment of the following working targets:

1. *Irrigation*

(*a*) Extension of new guls (Channels) 200 meters
to irrigate an additional area of   4.00 Acres

(b) Cleaning of old guls 100 meters to irrigate an additional area of · · · · · · · · · 6.00 Acres

(c) Construction of masonry wells—5 to irrigate an additional area of · · · · · · · 25.00 ,,

(d) Boring of wells—5 to irrigate an additional area of · · · · · · · · · · · 25.00 ,,

(e) Construction of one private tubewell—to irrigate an additional area of · · · · · 25.00 ,,

(f) Fitting of persian wheels on 5 bored wells to irrigate an additional area of · · · · 25.00 ,,

Total additional area proposed to be irrigated. 110.00 ,,

2. *Improved Seeds*

Distribution of improved seeds · · · · · 5.51 Tons

3. *Manures and Fertilizers*

(a) Nitrogenous fertilizers:
Distribution of Urea · · · · · · · · 3.00 Tons
Distribution of Ammonium sulphate · · 2.00 ,,
Distribution of calcium ammonium nitrate. 10.00 ,,

(b) Phosphatic fertilizers
Distribution of calcium ammonium nitrate 10.00 ,,

(c) Increase in area under green manuring · 45.00 Acres

(d) Construction of pucca compost pits and preparing compost · · · · · · · · · 54.00 ,,

(e) Planting of tree for fuel · · · · · · 200.00 ,,

4. *Improved Agricultural Practices*

Extension of area under Japanese method of paddy cultivation · · · · 20.00 Acres

Extension of area under improved method of wheat cultivation · · · · 100.00 ,,

Intensive cultivation in:

Bajra	20.00	,,
Maize	20.00	,,
Barley	20.00	,,
Upland paddy	10.00	,,

Total   190.00   ,,

Distribution of improved
   agricultural implements :

Cultivators	50 numbers
Singh Planks	10 numbers
Olpad threshers	5 numbers
Mould board ploughs	20 numbers
Hand hoes	100 numbers

5. *Land Reclamation*

Breaking Banjar land	2 Acres
Reclaiming water-logged area	10 Acres

6. *Soil Conservation Measures in*   100 Acres

7. *Controlling Pests and Diseases*

Termites	100 Acres
Other pests	50 Acres
Rats	(entire village)
Storing grain on scientific lines	73.53 Tons

Many a time working objectives may be achieved, but they may not lead to the attainment of the specific or fundamental objectives. The extension worker in the role of an evaluator, therefore, has to remain constantly on the watch so that not only the working objectives are achieved but the general and fundamental objectives are also achieved. If the latter are not being achieved, the reasons have to be discovered and analysed.

It sounds ridiculous that a fundamental objective is not being achieved even after the working or specific objectives are achieved. There can be two apparent reasons for it :

(i) The working objectives may have been achieved temporarily but their effect is not permanent and people revert to old things and practices.

Some common examples of this reversal in the programme of food production cited above could be :

(a) Digging and filling of compost pits. New pits are dug every year, but these pits give way after a year or two. The result is that the problem persists and in spite of continuous drives and emphasis, most of the villages still continue to store their manure in heaps.

(b) Decrease in the efficacy of improved seeds if they are not replaced quickly after they get degenerated and give lower production than before.

(c) Planting of fuel and fruit trees and their destruction as the result of driage and grazing.

(d) Adoption of improved agricultural practices temporarily and abandoning them after some time.

(ii) The working objectives may have been fulfilled but their achievement is offset by deficiency in some other sphere nullifying the effect of the achievement of the working or specific objectives.

Common examples of this in the programme of food production could be:

(a) Fall in food production in areas coming under consolidation offsetting the increase in production elsewhere. This is because no farmer likes to manure or effect any improvement in his fields for fear lest they should go to somebody else, at the time of preparation of chaks (blocks).

(b) Increase in area under water-logging and salinity with increase in canal irrigation, construction of railway lines, irrigation channels, roads, dams, embankments, *etc.*

(c) Increase in the prevalence of pests and diseases.

(d) Increase in area under sugarcane and other cash crops at the expense of food crops.

(e) Frequent occurrence of adverse weather conditions.

(f) New irrigation works reducing area under irrigation from the existing irrigation sources with the result that overall irrigated area does not increase although such works may be a more certain source of irrigation.

(g) Temporary fall in production due to impending land reforms causing considerable uncertainty in the minds of farmers.

(h) Increase in cattle population and their grazing menace.

(i) Decrease in cultivated area.

(j) Fertile areas near cities and villages going out of cultivation for expansion and in their place marginal or sub-marginal lands coming under the plough.

What to Evaluate?

Evaluation for the acceptance of a programme by the people involves the study of :

    (*i*) The reactions of the staff working out the programme.

    (*ii*) The reactions of the village leaders.

    (*iii*) The reactions of the people affected and those not affected by the programme.

    (*iv*) The reactions of the independent observers.

    (*v*) Number of people affected by the programme.

    (*vi*) Cost-benefit or input-output ratio.

    (*vii*) Direct or indirect cultural, social, leadership and economic changes brought about by the programme.

  (*viii*) The methods, means and techniques followed.

    (*ix*) Participation of the people and workers manning the programme.

The extension worker should constantly study and evaluate all his programmes on the above lines and modify his methods, means and techniques to get quicker success.

Study of the personal difficulties of the workers

This is one of the most important items to be studied and evaluated. Asking about and finding out personal difficulties of the workers brings a senior worker nearer to them. Senior workers have to view the difficulties of their junior workers by placing themselves in their position. Many senior workers in course of time wean themselves away from the hearts of the junior workers with the result they never get their full support and willing participation in the work.

If the personal and other difficulties of the extension workers are not removed, their hearts and minds are distracted from the work. They live worried and do not feel at one with the programme. A block development officer once told me his case history in one of the inter-state seminars where we had met. He said that he had been getting his initial pay of the post of the block development officer for more than five years without getting any increment. He had since two more children. Although his liability had considerably increased, there was no corresponding increase in his pay as the Accountant General had refused to give him any annual increment unless a certificate from government was forthcoming for giving him advance increment sanctioned at the start of his service. The headquarter was not ready to give him such a certificate as the copy of the required government order was not traceable in the files. The office searched for the copy of the Government order several times but it could not lay its hands on it. It also did not bother to think of any other alternative by which he would get his increment. He contacted his higher officers at the State headquarters several times. Every time he contacted them, they sent a note to the office, but whenever any such note reached the office, the clerks felt greatly annoyed and even showed him their displeasure as to why he had reported the matter to the senior officers. This state of affairs had been continuing for the last five years. By this time, he had spent more than Rs. 200 in corresponding with the Accountant General and other officers and in undertaking journey to contact the district and headquarter officers. He went on to say, "You cannot imagine my plight when I go to my house in the evening and see the mental agony of my wife and hear her taunts and sarcastic remarks against me and government. What can that poor lady do, when she was not able to meet the family expenditure? The shortage of money haunts me even in my sleep for I am in debt now. My children remain half-starved, poorly clothed and without text-books in the school."

As he told me this, tears flowed from his eyes and his lips began to quiver with emotion to relieve him temporarily of his mental agony.

The above is only a solitary case cited, but there are many unknown cases like this which do not see the light of the day and come to the notice of those who count. Many of such persons suffer unheard and unnoticed. How could such a Block Development Officer or any other man in his position put his soul and mind in his work when he was in debt and knowing that he is entitled to the payment but he is not getting it in spite of his hard and sincere work?

Evaluation of such personal difficulties should be given the top priority for creating proper condition of work. The early removal of these personal difficulties always leads to great satisfaction and contentment among the workers and they try to work harder and more enthusiastically when they are reasonably free from personal worries. There should be no greater satisfaction to a senior officer than when his junior officers feel that their future is entirely safe in his hands.

Evaluation of guidance received by the workers

Do the workers receive proper superior guidance or not, is also an important aspect which is necessary to be evaluated. One cannot build up his subordinates or the people unless he guides them and also constantly seeks some guidance from his superior officers or the people's representatives or people themselves. Guidance like extension education is also a two-way process. It has to be given as well as sought.

Guidance is often confused with inspection. In extension, there has to be more of guidance than inspection. If a worker has received proper and timely guidance, his work does not very much need to be inspected. If only senior workers ensure proper and timely guidance, the work of inspection is greatly reduced. Inspection in the absence of guidance does more harm than good. Often it leads to false work and reporting and even spoils the attitude of workers and the people.

If after evaluation it is found that *a particular level of worker* is unable to give *any* adequate guidance to his subordinate workers or the people, he should immediately be given an in-service training in that programme to enable him to give the required guidance.

(j) As a researcher

The extension worker in the role of a researcher has to carry out researches in the fields more by observing things than by doing and laying out experiments himself. He has to be a keen observer and listener, observing and listening to things wherever he moves about. He has to pick up what is good for him and for the people and communicate the same to the community/villages where his observation would be of use to them. These observing experiences are the most valuable experiences for field workers as they can never be collected from any other source or place.

A field observer once observed that the incidence of attack of *Gundhy bug* was the least in paddy crops sown in lines and properly inter-cultured. This was a very valuable observation which was afterwards taken advantage of to convince the people for transplanting paddy in lines and carrying out inter-culture. Many of such field experiences are so valuable that they greatly help in orienting and changing the views of the specialists and people who are far away from the field. As soon as an extension worker makes any important observation, he should immediately record it and send it to his senior officer for comparing this observation from the reports received from elsewhere and for communicating the same to other workers for their benefit.

There is a variety of mango called *Chausa*. It is a late maturing variety. On account of this, it fetches a very high price in the market. Although it brings good economic returns, it is a poor bearer. Research workers were anxious to develop its fruit bearing capacity. They could not succeed. In a seminar organised by the Uttar Pradesh Fruit Development Board at Meerut in the month of July 1961, this problem was posed. One experienced orchardist came out with his experience and said that if *Chausa* orchards were irrigated two times during the winter season, their fruit bearing capacity would increase considerably. He added that he had been following that practice since long with good success. It is the experience of this kind that the extension worker has to collect. His research laboratory is not in any special building or field, but the large number of people, their houses and their fields serve as a vast laboratory to him where numerous minds working silently, unnoticed, unheard and unaided get maturer and maturer in experience and in that process unfold several secrets of nature which it is difficult for the expensive laboratories to do.

It has been observed that findings, as given out by the research, do not exactly suit all local conditions. They need several modifications before they could be adopted by the people. The extension worker, therefore, has to be very careful in finding out at the earliest opportunity the changes that are required to be made in a particular recommendation or technique or method of work. If he can modify them himself, he should do it immediately and communicate his modifications, experience or even difficulties to his higher officers for their advice or information. Often people themselves make their own changes. Such modifications and changes have to be closely observed, utilised in other areas and communicated to higher authorities for utilisation elsewhere.

The Bakshi-Ka-Talab smokeless *Choolah* (hearth) when it was given out for adoption in the villages after considerable researches at Bakshi-Ka-Talab (Lucknow), failed at most of the places, because it did not suit local conditions. A *Panchayat* Secretary of Goshaingaij block in Lucknow district of Uttar Pradesh studied the various difficulties being encountered in this programme and modified the design of the smokeless *choolah* to suit local conditions. He provided a tin sheet on the top of the outlet and widened the outlet besides providing a screen for preventing the fire to go to the second hole of the *choolah*. The modified *choolah* was very much liked by the people and it came to be adopted in almost all the houses in two of his villages. The modification made by the extension worker in this case was so valuable that it helped a great deal in the extension of the programme. Suitable modifications if required should always be made by the extension worker in all the recommendations, techniques or methods given out by the research worker before they could be applicable to the local conditions. The programmes have been generally found failing where the extension worker is not himself experienced in the details of the programme and only acts as an adviser to the people. People who try out the recommendation, fail because they are not properly trained in how to remove their difficulties which they face in the execution of the programme.

Some people in the rural areas or elsewhere are always in the habit of making silent researches. They discover new things mainly by their keen observation. Some of these researches, or experiences are very valuable. The extension worker should be in the habit of collecting information about all these researches and experiences made by the people and take advantage of them for making suitable modifications and adjustments in programmes. He should also communicate details of these local researches and experiences made by the people and take advantage of them for making suitable modifications and adjustments in programmes. He should also communicate details of these local researches and experiences to his higher officers so that they may be taken advantage of elsewhere.

THE EXTENSION WORKER—A HUMAN BEING

The extension worker is one of the most important workers of government interpreting its policies and programmes to the people and in turn relaying their problems, reactions and requirements to government. He is a link between the two and is in a way a key person for government; for if he fails in any of his duties, government is likely to be misunderstood by the people who would remain dissatisfied.

In performing his duties well, he serves government as well as the people directly. To discharge his duties well, he has to be properly oriented, educated, helped and guided constantly in all that he needs. He has also to be kept free from worries and anxieties about his job. Those, therefore, who are responsible for supervising the work of the extension workers have a great responsibility upon themselves. They have to ensure that the extension workers who have their field of work in the rural areas with difficult living conditions, are relieved of all reasonable personal difficulties and inconveniences which prevent them from putting their best in the work.

He is also to be provided with necessary working facilities and kept well contented, and if he is not, he would not be discharging his duties according to expectations. Some of the working difficulties with which the extension workers are commonly faced are:

(1) Their transfer at a time when their children are in the middle of the school year—such transfers cause lot of unplanned expenditure and annoyance to the extension workers.

(2) Lack of educational facilities for their children. If at any place, there is no nearby school, some allowance should be given for educating their children somewhere.

(3) Inadequate touring facilities.

　(a) Inadequate travelling grant.

　(b) Delay in payment of travelling bills.

　(c) Lack of facilities for touring in the rural areas, but on the other hand, too much insistence on night halts. It would have been much better, if in rural areas, *Panchayat Ghars,* if not all but a certain percentage, were provided by government with some lodging facilities for the touring staff. Such a measure could have greatly added to the efficiency of the workers. At present they hesitate in staying in villages on account of party politics. The difficulty is all the more serious with lady workers.

(4) Lack of medical facilities.

(5) Delay in confirmation cases.

(6) Delay in settling representations. A representation should normally be settled within two months.

(7) Delay in pay fixation cases.

(8) Existence of rules in which a temporary government servant, if promoted, starts on his new post from the lowest scale of the new grade even though it is lower than his existing pay. The workers break in their patience if they find that promotion means less pay for the present or even after a few year's service, they get less pay for some reason or other.

(9) Inadequate technical guidance.

(10) Lack of sympathetic approach to irregularities committed unknowingly in good faith in the interest of work.

(11) Lack of adequate residential accommodation.

These are some of the important points which if not attended to in good time, demoralise the workers and lead to innumerable wrong tendencies detrimental to the discharge of their functions. One such tendency is that they do not put in their best and spend their money and official and private time in getting things corrected or expedited and in seeking interviews with seniors or getting their grievances removed through authorised or unauthorised agencies. It is, therefore, necessary that the difficulties of the types mentioned above, are looked into and dealt with expeditiously to give the workers a working confidence and contentment.

Some people think that as soon as a worker is on government's pay roll, he ceases to be a free man having any aspirations, and he is just a slave who could be given commands to obey quietly. Most of the workers would perhaps prefer to be less paid than go without shelter, proper education of their children, proper care of their families when they go on tour and timely medical aid.

The extension worker is a human being and not a machine which is fed at one end with raw materials and which turns out finished products at the other according to plan. Many people consider the extension worker to be a machine. They think that all instructions issued by them for adoption of the programmes should be implemented by him like a machine. These people forget, that the extension worker has to interpret their orders or ideas to the people and convince them for their adoption. People have their own circumstances and resources which differ from person to person. As against dead machines, the people are living machines which respond only to the extent the order/instruction/programme suits them according to their circumstances and resources. In the case of dead machines, the circumstances and resources are fixed and do not change until there is disorder. This is one of the most important fundamental points in extension which is very often lost sight of. Those who behave in this way, should think that, perhaps, their services were not needed, had all extension workers and the people behaved like a dead machine and everything turned out per order.

Some people contend that government have supreme power and need to have the same rule for everybody and for all situations for the sake of equity and justice. Nobody can question this contention, for government is expected to be impartial to all. Even within the frame-work of this principle, things can be adjusted in a way that there is least dislocation or difficulty to the extension worker provided those who could help have a sympathetic heart and helping attitude and act after thinking what they would have expected if they would have been in that position. Things go bad when thinking is rigid and mechanical and extension worker is considered a dead machine and not a human being.

Rules and regulations have to be there and should be strictly enforced. They should, however, be drafted in a way that people for whom they are meant, put in their best. If they result in frustration and dissatisfaction and tend to lower the output of work, the purpose of making them is defeated. There should be a periodical review of the existing rules and regulations to modify them to suit the changing circumstances, working convenience and human psychology. To meet this end, they have to be slightly flexible. Implementation of such flexibilities, if necessary, may be left to the discretion of some high powered committee which should be able to take stock of the difficulty and remedy the situation. What is necessary is to keep the human machinery well oiled and geared to enable it to put in its best. It is often said that people do not live by bread alone and if it is true, something more than the bread would have to be provided to keep them in a fit condition.

INDEX

185